The Complete Video Course

The Complete
Video Course
Third Edition

Keith Brookes

BⓈXTREE

First published in 1989 by Boxtree Limited

First published in paperback in 1990
Second edition published in 1992
Third edition published in 1995

1 2 3 4 5 6 7 8 9 10

Designed by Blackjacks Limited
Printed and bound in Great Britain by
Cox & Wyman Ltd, Reading, Berkshire

Boxtree Limited
Broadwall House
21 Broadwall
London SE1 9PL

A CIP catalogue entry for this book is available from the British Library.

ISBN 1 85283 914 7

Front cover photograph courtesy of Samsung Electronics (UK) Ltd.

Contents

Introduction

Video camcorders are remarkable products of modern technology. Although even the simplest models are, by any standards, sophisticated pieces of equipment, all are designed to make moving picture taking easy. So although they may seem at first glance to be complicated machines with a bewildering array of controls, you will find that they are very simple to use. Camcorders take the form of lightweight one-piece camera units which incorporate their own video recorders. They can play back recordings over their viewfinders, which enables you to check your results as you go along. To record the sound, a built-in microphone is also provided.

If you are new to creative video, you will find that making movies is a hobby which can be enjoyed in many different ways. Perhaps your ambitions extend no further than taking moving snapshots of your family? Video is certainly the ideal medium for recording memories: high days and holidays, big events and quiet moments are all suitable subjects for movies. Video brings memories alive in a way which is simply not possible with any other kind of camera, no matter how complex and expensive.

It is important to be aware of the many technical facilities on today's camcorders and to know how to make the most of them. Take note of the advice which follows on a wide range of topics such as lighting, composition and special effects. There is more to movie making than the taking of pictures, though, and here you will find instructions on all the other techniques which go to make personal movies into polished productions: how to plan your sequences to form connected stories; how to record better sound; and how to edit video and carry out additional post-production work on your tapes such as adding commentary. If you have not yet decided on your first camcorder and are confused as to what to buy, turn to

Chapter 1 for information on which format is 'best' and which camera features are really useful.

Given that the equipment is used with skill and under-standing, in fact, amateur video is now able to attain a standard which bears comparison with the professional work which we see every day on our television screens. And the scope, of course, need not be restricted to the shooting of family records. The range of subjects which can be tackled is limited only by your imagination! With the application of a little pre-planning, some extra effort at the shooting stage and perhaps even a complete re-arrangement of the shots at an editing stage, holiday videos can be turned into travel documentaries, events in your home town can be recorded as local newsreels, and you could join together with your friends to produce your own dramas.

Getting into home video-making has never been easier. Whether you are a video snap-shotter, a gadget freak or feel serious about movie-making, you will find it a fascinating leisure activity.

Keith Brookes

Help with choosing your first camcorder

Origins

It's strange but true: the earliest ancestors of the video camcorder are to be found in holes deep below ground which were inhabited by cave dwellers long before the dawn of recorded history. Here, faint traces can still be found of man-made images which show that, in one respect at least, our club-wielding predecessors were just like us: they had the urge to record the important happenings in their lives in the form of two-dimensional pictures.

The creation of the early drawings required considerable ability on the part of the artist. More recently, the coming of photography has made it possible for even the least talented among us to produce our own pictorial records. Now we have video, a complex technology which is so automated and fool-proofed that it enables anyone, whether technically minded or not, to record moving pictures to a standard which can be very high indeed.

Although camcorders have become a popular means of picture-taking, many more people are familiar with video in the form of table-top recorders (VCRs) for the time-shifting of television programmes and the viewing of rented films. If you have used one of these, you will already know quite a bit about video recording from handling video cassettes, and knowing what all the tape control buttons are for. Also, you will no doubt be aware that video tapes and their cassettes come in various formats, and that the initials VHS, for instance, stand for one of the most popular of these. However, for the benefit of those who have yet to become acquainted with these mysteries, let's take a look at the whole business of video formats and their particular significance to anyone who is intending to purchase a camcorder.

Choosing a format

Currently, there are six formats which can be used with camcorders. These are Standard VHS, VHS-C, Super VHS, Super-VHS-C, 8mm and Hi8. Various other formats have come and gone over the years, but these are the ones which have become established and likely to remain for the foreseeable future.

How do you set about choosing the best format? Let's consider each in turn, taking 8mm first.

8mm/Hi8

The 8mm format, or Video 8 as it is sometimes called, has become a leading format for amateur camcorder users. Its cassettes, which are similar to audio cassettes in size, are incompatible with the VHS format and so cannot be played back on VHS machines. The 8mm-wide cassette tapes are specially produced 'metallic' types and, in spite of their narrower width, the recording quality is at least equal to VHS. 8mm tapes have a maximum runtime of two hours when run at Standard Play or four hours at LP speed ('PAL' machines). At the LP setting, the tape speed is halved to double the runtime, albeit at the cost of a slight reduction in picture quality.

In spite of its up to four-hour capability, 8mm is basically a camcorder-only format, there being few 8mm table-top VCRs around. To view your own recordings, you can play them back directly off the camcorder on to your television set by connecting it either to the TV's aerial socket or, preferably, to the AV sockets if your television has these direct audio and video connections which give better picture quality. Alternatively, you can copy the recording on to a VHS cassette for showing along with your ordinary tapes if you have a VHS VCR. This copying involves a slight loss of picture quality, but if it is done as a part of an editing routine (see page 108), the loss is then offset by the improvement in presentation that editing always brings.

One of the big pluses for 8mm video is its high audio quality due to the FM hi-fi system it uses for recording both mono and stereo sound. This encodes the audio and video signals together at different levels within the depth of the tape coating via the high-speed rotation of the head-drum; it is this 'high writing speed' recording method which gives the audio its excellent fidelity. However, the combination of the two signals in this way does have one drawback: it prevents new sound from being audio dubbed (erased and re-recorded) without affecting the pictures during editing. For this reason, you will not find an audio dub button on 8mm machines except for the few which have the PCM audio recording system.

Hi8 is the 'super' or 'high band' version of the 8mm format. The picture quality is even better than the standard format due to the use of specially formulated tapes and by technical upgrading

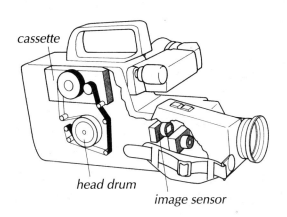

Your camcorder consists of a video camera and recorder built as a one-piece unit. Behind the lens is the electronic image-sensor; the rear of the body-shell accommodates the cassette, tape transport mechanisms and record-section.

The shape shown here is one of the newer ultra-compact palmcorders.

of the machines themselves – so both the tapes and the equipment to run them cost more. Hi-fi stereo sound recording is standard on this format. To reap the full benefit of the extra quality recording, the camcorder should be connected for playback to a television with an S-Video socket. By this means, the TV receives and is capable of handling the brightness and colour components of the video signal separately. This prevents interaction between the two and so improves the resolution of the picture detail as compared with the standard 8mm format, which handles its picture signals in composite form.

Standard VHS/S-VHS

If you already have a table-top **VHS** VCR it might seem sensible to buy a camcorder of the same tape format so that you can play back your camera recordings on the same machine as your other video tapes. Although this is an advantage it is not, however, a conclusive reason to choose standard VHS as the format for your camcorder since, as for 8mm, you can if you wish play your recordings directly on to your TV from off the camcorder instead of using a VCR.

One plus-point for the format, though, is that you can record up to five hours of material on to one tape at Standard Play speed. Also, the cassettes are cheaper, comparatively, than any of the other formats, blank tape being widely available in a variety of qualities which extend up to the 'PRO' grade for important record-ings. Picture quality is good and, on camcorders, sound recorded as mono in the form of an independent linear edgetrack can be audio-dubbed without affecting the picture recording – an impor-tant advantage when video tapes are being edited (see page 98). Since the mono track runs at the slow forward speed of the tape, the sound tends to be slightly hissy compared to 8mm audio, but this is not normally a problem on a good recording.

S-VHS is the 'Super', or 'high band', VHS format, and the improvement in picture quality is similar to that of Hi8 over 8mm. As for Hi8, playback should be viewed on a television fitted with an S-Video connector, either directly from off the camcorder or from off an S-VHS VCR. Sound recording is available in both mono (which can be audio-dubbed), and hi-fi FM stereo depending on the model. Note that S-VHS recordings will not play back on a standard VHS machine; standard VHS tapes will, however, play back on S-VHS machines at low-band quality.

VHS and S-VHS çassettes are bulky, and camcorders to fit these are correspondingly hefty pieces of equipment to carry round. Mainly because of this, VHS/S-VHS has largely gone out of favour for amateur camcorder use and has effectively become a professional format.

VHS-C/S-VHS-C

VHS-C is the compact version of the Standard VHS format. Technically speaking, the only difference between VHS and VHS-C is in the length of tape in the cassette, which for VHS-C is currently limited to a runtime of forty-five minutes at Standard Play speed, ninety minutes at LP speed. Because of the shorter tape length, the cassettes are much reduced in size and VHS-C camcorders are therefore similar in portability to 8mm machines. They also have an advantage over 8mm in being playable on full-size VCRs via an adapter which adjusts the tape-path to suit. Most VHS-C camcorders are twin-speed machines to maximise tape runtime.

S-VHS-C is the 'super' version of VHS-C, and is capable of delivering the same picture quality as S-VHS and Hi8.

Choosing a Camcorder

Having considered the tape formats, now let's take a look at the camcorders that use the tapes. There is a very wide range of models to choose from, and they come in all shapes, sizes and prices. In fact, the choice is so wide that your problem may be one of bewilderment – how are you to pick the ideal model from the dozens competing for your custom? We have already narrowed the field significantly by looking at cassette formats.

Video formats – pros and cons

	runtime per cassette (PAL)	cost of tape	picture quality
8mm	2 hours (SP) 4 hours (LP)	average	good
Hi8	as 8mm	high	excellent
Standard VHS	up to 5 hours (SP)	low	good
VHS-C	45 mins (SP) 1½ hr (LP)	high	good
Super-VHS	up to 4 hrs (SP)	high	excellent
Super-VHS-C	as VHS-C	high	excellent

Now we'll narrow it some more by considering which camcorder features are essential and which are simply desirable.

In essence, a camcorder consists of a video camera and a recorder built together into a one-piece unit which can be powered either by battery or mains adaptor. This distinguishes camcorders from 'separates', which do the same job but in the form of individual cable-connected cameras and recorders. For some years now, the amateur market has been dominated by one-piece machines and separates have virtually disappeared from the scene.

The camera section of a camcorder has a photographic lens which forms an image of the subject on a sensing device. This converts the image into electronic signals which are passed to the recorder section containing the cassette housing and tape transport mechanisms. The video sensing is done by a robust and high-definition solid-state imaging device called a CCD. The recorder section also receives sound signals from a built-in microphone and puts these onto the tape along with the video pictures.

Camcorders can play back their recordings immediately after they have put them onto the tape. The playback can be displayed either over the viewfinder – so you can check your recordings as you go – or by being connected to an

sound quality	size
excellent	compact
excellent	compact
good	bulky but steady to hold
good (mono) excellent (hi-fi)	compact
good (mono) excellent (hi-fi)	as VHS
good (mono) excellent (hi-fi)	compact

external television screen or monitor. One main distinction between camcorder types is in the style of the body-shell. Most camcorders are designed to be hand held, so the minimisation of size and weight has been an important consideration. However, the lighter the camera, the harder it is to hold steady. Professional style camcorders like the full-size VHS and S-VHS machines are quite bulky and heavy, but being longer in the body, they can be supported on the shoulder leaving the operator's hands clear to give further steadying at the front end and work the controls. At the other end of the scale, to help lightweight camcorders deliver steady pictures, the designers have developed electronic, optical and mechanical means of offsetting camera shake, ie: *image stabilizers,* which are now being built into many machines.

Camcorder *viewfinders* are, in effect, miniature television screens, and they show both the scene as received by the camcorder lens and also the recorded picture when the machine is switched to playback. Some viewfinders are built solidly into the camcorder body while others are adjustable to make it easier to take shots at awkward angles. Although most still display the scene in monochrome, an increasing number of new camcorder models have colour viewfinders. Some have conventional eyepieces, while others so-called 'sports' viewfinders – allow viewing of a magnified image with the eye away from the eyepiece. The latest development is for viewfinders with relatively large LCD screen displays which allow the camcorder to double as a colour playback monitor. Viewfinders also display a range of useful information to help operate the machine. We shall be examining these in detail in Chapter 2.

Operating features

So far, we have looked briefly at the basics which are common to all camcorders, that is formats, body-shapes and viewfinder arrangements. Now let's take a quick look at some of the operating features which you need to know about before you can decide on the model of machine which will be best suited to your particular needs.

To begin with, all camcorders have *automatic exposure control* as standard. Auto-exposure systems work by measuring the average brightness of the incoming picture, and they control it to a standard level by varying the lens iris opening and the 'gain' of the camcorder's video amplifier. In most situations this works perfectly well, but there are times when it is useful to be able to make your own adjustments. Most camcorders provide manual control options to allow you to do this.

The simplest of these manual controls is the *backlight* (BLC) button, by which the exposure can be increased by a fixed amount when shots are taken under 'backlit' lighting conditions (see page 29). On some recent models, automatic backlight control is provided instead of manual. As an alternative, fuller and more flexible *manual exposure control* is featured on some machines, usually in the form of a thumbheel. This enables you to control the amount of increase or decrease in the iris opening and so obtain the best possible picture. As a further element of control,

Check list

Here are a few really useful features – check your model has them before you buy.

- *A socket for an extension microphone – a useful means of improving the quality of your sound recordings.*

- *An earpiece socket – essential for monitoring the sound as it goes onto the tape.*

- *A record-review button – a great time and battery saver when you want to make a quick check-replay of a shot on location.*

- *A manual focus ring and zoom lever for fast operation and minimum drain on battery.*

a few models have a 'gain up' switch which increases the gain of the camcorder's video amplifier; this is useful in poor lighting conditions but it is generally at the expense of a more grainy picture. Yet another refinement found on some models is *'exposure lock'* by means of which the exposure can be preset at a particular level and held through a shot; we shall consider the reasons for wishing to do this later (see Chapter 5).

Many video cameras now include a feature known as *high speed shutter*. This is primarily intended for the recording of fast-moving subjects such as sports action. The normal (electronic) shutter speed of a camcorder is 1/50th of a second. This is too slow to record rapid movement as anything other than a blur. Higher shutter speeds, variable up to 1/10000th of a second or beyond, are now available on camcorders to give better definition of fast action when played back on a VCR with matching replay facilities. However, high shutter speeds reduce the exposure time and so are best used only in good light. Also, the movement on screen can appear rather jerky due to an effect known as 'image strobing'. On the other hand, the details within the shot can certainly be seen with enhanced clarity if played back frame-by-frame or in slow motion.

Slow shutter, a recent variant, has its uses in low light recording conditions and its tendency to smear the image of bright moving subjects can also be exploited as a special effect.

The use of high speed shutter technology has been extended by the introduction of *Program auto-exposure* (AE) systems on some camcorders. These programs give the user various exposure options suited to the needs of differing subjects, typically sports and portraiture. For Sport AE, a high shutter speed is set automatically and the auto-exposure then opens up the lens to suit. Conversely, Portrait AE sets a larger than normal aperture. This gives the picture a reduced depth of field and so separates the subject from the background; the shutter speed is then automatically adjusted to offset the increased exposure. There are differences of opinion as to the real worth of Program AE for video recording, but most people agree that some form of manual override of auto-exposure control is a very useful thing to have on any camcorder.

Camcorders vary in their ability to produce a good picture in low light, but any model capable of working at a light level of 10 lux or less will enable you to record in most interiors without the need for additional lighting. To help you cope with really poor lighting, some models are fitted with a small *onboard video light* for either manual or automatic control.

The ability to fade both vision and sound while shooting is certainly a worthwhile feature, and *auto-faders* are to be found on almost all camcorders. If you can, you should try this out before you buy; some may give incomplete or premature fading of the sound, while others (a minority) fade to white instead of black. Some recent models give the option of fading to a mosaic effect.

For many years, video camera lenses came with *manual focus rings* and *zoom operating levers* as standard. However, the pattern has changed, and many camcorders now have the usual power zoom toggles but no zoom lever; another change is the substitution of servo-operated manual focus controls in place of a simple focus ring, These arrangements work well enough, but some prefer the direct manual alternatives, partly because power-driven controls use up precious battery capacity.

Modern camcorders have *zoom lenses* which can enlarge the scene by telephoto factors of x8 or more. Some now have *zoom extenders* which further increase the zoom range by electronic means up to as much as x100. As we shall see in Chapter 4, hand-held shots taken at extreme telephoto ranges can be pretty wobbly affairs. So the practical value of greatly extended zoom ranges is somewhat open to question, though electronic zooms can be used for the creation of special effects. Although the field of view of a normal video zoom lens set at maximum wide angle compares with the standard 50mm lens found on many SLR still cameras, there are wide angle attachment lenses to give a wide angle zoom setting, giving a significantly wider view – a useful feature in tight situations or when really wide shots are needed. *Macro*, a lens setting which enables the shooting of small subjects (including colour transparencies) at very close range, is also to be found on most camcorders. Control takes the form of either an extension of the simple zoom lever or, more recently, a 'macro button' which does the job in a slightly different way.

Although manual focus is a useful feature, almost all camcorder operation is done with the lens set to *auto focus* (AF). This is a great boon to the amateur camera operator who, unlike the professional film maker, has to get by without an assistant to act a focus-puller. Most current AF systems are both accurate and fast in finding and holding focus on moving subjects, and although there are a number of different types of system, there is not too much to choose between them in practice.

Another 'camera' feature is the *white balance* (WB) setting system which compensates for changes in the colour of the light while shooting, a situation which is described on page 40. The most popular type is the fully auto WB which monitors the scene and continuously corrects for any light changes. This is commonly supplemented by two or more fixed presets, one for daylight, one for artificial (tungsten) light and sometimes one for fluorescent light. Some systems are to set to the lighting condition by being aimed at a standard reference such as a white card or lens cap viewed under the lighting. A few camcorders feature *WB lock,* a useful refinement by means of which a setting can be first obtained and then held irrespective of lighting changes – handy when you are shooting sunsets!

Moving on now to some of the other facilities and controls to be found on camcorders, there are one or two which deserve a mention here because of the way in which they speed up and simplify their operation. A *full auto* button, for instance, is very useful because it gives auto-exposure/auto focus/auto white balance at a single press. Another helpful facility is called *picture search.* Its function is similar to the one found on table top video machines, and it enables the recorded picture to be replayed over the viewfinder both forwards or in reverse at a fast speed so that particular points on the tape can be located quickly. A refinement of this is *record review* or *quick review* which automatically replays the last few seconds of the previous shot as a check before returning the camcorder to record-mode.

Rehearsal or *Monitor* mode is also very useful, as it saves the mechanism and tape from unnecessary wear by displaying the scene to be shot in the viewfinder without the camcorder needing to be held in record-pause while takes are being lined up.

If you are 'editing in camera', that is shooting your scenes to the correct length and in the correct order, the *still frame* button will help you begin each new shot at the right place on the tape. Some upmarket machines have *digital still*, giving freeze-frames without the customary noise-bars, others have *still frame advance*, to make the finding of edit-in points even more precise. *Time lapse*, as its name suggests, makes possible recording in bursts of a few frames at various time intervals so subjects such as the movement of clouds or the budding of flowers can be studied in speed-up replay.

Digital title superimposers or *character-generators* are provided on most camcorders. These enable you to put titles onto your recordings while they are being shot, with the option of adding a record of the date and time if desired. Digital effects such as *wipe* (an alternative to the fade), *strobe* (which gives a jerky effect), *mosaic* (which adds a chequerboard appearance), and *solarisation* (which adds an oil painting-like quality), are all image-juggling tricks to be used sparingly. *Cinema mode* blanks off portions of the top and bottom of the picture to yield a quasi widescreen effect, while *digital filters* can be used to shoot in monochrome or old-style sepia.

Sound recording and other facilities

We should not overlook the sound recording facilities when choosing a camcorder. All camcorders are fitted with an *onboard microphone*, and many but not all have a socket for monitoring the incoming or recorded sound on an *earpiece* or *headphones*; many also provide a socket for plugging in an *extension micro-phone*. A problem with camcorders in general is the proximity of the onboard microphone to emitters of mechanical noise such as the camera's power zoom or head-drum motor. Some machines have less trouble with this than others, but the option of being able to use an extension microphone held well away from the camcorder is a good way of avoiding spoiling your recordings. There is more on this topic in Chapter 10.

Another sound recording problem is wind-noise on the microphone, and some camcorders are provided with a *wind-noise filter*, which, when switched in, can help reduce this annoying fault. While on the subject of camcorders and their microphones, some models, as we have already noted, now record sound in *hi-fi stereo*, and the audio quality is excellent. You do, of course, need to have replay facilities which also have stereo sound to do justice to this type of audio recording.

You may regard *audio dub* as an essential camcorder feature. Many VHS-format machines have this, and some also have *insert edit,* over-recording of the original picture without affecting the sound. 8mm-format machines, however, where they have insert, replace both pictures and sound together. For all insert editing operations, the feature known as *flying erase* is essential, as it enables the edits to be made cleanly without disturbance at the insert out-point. One of the newest camcorder operating features is *Random Assemble Edit* (RAE), a facility which converts it, when used as a replay machine in an editing set-up, into a simple edit controller: it will automatically play back shots in the required order onto a re-recording VCR, the operation of which is also under its control. To keep the head-drum happy, *auto head clean* is to be found on some machines.

Although the essential control buttons will be found on the camcorder body, quite a few of the less-used ones are often located on the camcorder remote control. As for the sockets to connect your machine to the outside world, the most important are: an *RF out* socket for connecting it to the television set for the replay of tapes; *AV out* sockets for connection to your TV's *AV in* sockets (if it has these) for higher quality playback; an *S-Video Terminal* for the replay of high-band recordings on a TV set with an S-Video in socket. For editing, your camcorder may have a *synchro-edit* socket for synchronised starting as a replay machine together with a matching VCR acting as re-recording machine; or alternatively, a Control L Terminal or its equivalent for automatic control of camcorder and VCR by an edit controller.

To end this features roundup, we need to mention *timecode generation* facilities (VITC or RCTC) for frame-accurate editing – see Chapter 8 for more on this new development; *edit switch* for optimising your camcorder's video signal output when copying tapes onto another machine; and *SP/LP* sliders to switch you from standard recording speed to long play.

As you can see, there are a lot of things to keep in mind when you are choosing a camcorder. Fortunately, it's simpler than it looks. First decide on the video format, and then jot down a shortlist of the features you consider to be really essential bearing in mind the cost of the models which include them. Having narrowed the field, do a tour of the shops and try as many different models as you can, keeping a watchful eye on such essentials as good picture definition and colour, no picture 'jitter' (unsteadiness), and good sound recording with low hiss and mechanical noise pick-up.

Whatever you decide, it pays to look before you leap. At the end of the day, a camcorder with sound basic design is going to give you years of creative pleasure, even if it doesn't have all the latest sales gimmicks!

2 Camcorder Day One

The arrival of a brand new camcorder is a red letter day in the life of any household. The impulse to take it out of the box and start taking pictures right away can be very strong, and the user-friendliness of these machines is such that it is quite possible to do just that.

It is better, though, for you to restrain your natural impatience to make a start, and take time instead to read the book of instructions before you begin pressing any of the buttons. This is important if you are to gain a proper understanding of how to obtain the best results from your new machine, and it also contains some cautionary notes to help you avoid accidentally damaging it through misuse.

The instruction details will differ from model to model, but the basics are much the same for all. Camcorders have two main functions: recording and playing back. The instruction book will probably devote its two principal sections to these, preceding them with guidance on how to prepare your machine for action.

In addition, you will find step-by-step directions on how to connect the camcorder to a colour television for playback, and how to operate special functions such as fades and inserts. You will find advice on how to couple your camcorder to a second video machine to enable you to copy your tapes and carry out editing operations.

Fitting the Battery

It may all look a little complicated at first, but camcorders are quite simple things to use if you tackle the job in an orderly fashion. The first task, you will discover, is to find and fit the rechargeable battery. It will be stowed either in the carrying case or within a plastic container. The thing to remember about these batteries is that they should be stored in a way which prevents the

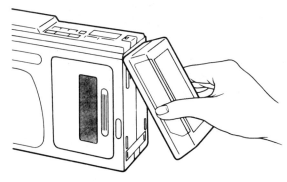

After charging, the new battery is fitted into place on the camcorder. Some batteries fit on the end of the camcorder body as shown, others clip onto the side, and still others slot into a compartment within the machine. Take care to follow exactly the battery fitting instructions for your particular model.

When the camcorder battery warning light comes on, recharge the battery to ensure that it is ready for the next time it is needed. This charger is dealing with two batteries at once.

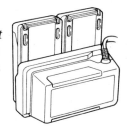

With a fully-charged battery in place, the blank cassette can be loaded for recording. Before you do so, make sure that the cassette's safety-tab has not been removed.

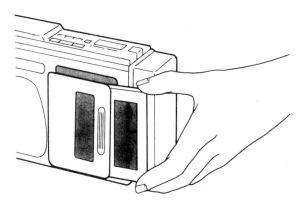

accidental short-circuiting of their contact terminals: if they are shorted, the battery quickly overheats and will become unfit for further use.

The next job is to check on the battery. This will probably have been supplied discharged. To confirm this, clip it into place on the camcorder as directed, and switch on. If the camcorder fails to respond, the battery needs to be put on charge. Another, and perhaps better way to make the check is to clip the battery into the mains charger; switch this on, and watch to see if the charge lamp goes out. If it does, the battery is ready for immediate use; if not, leave it on charge for as long as necessary.

With the fully charged battery in place, you are now ready to load a tape cassette, following the instructions. If by any chance the cassette has already been used for recording on another machine (for example, on a VHS mains VCR), remember to check that the cassette's safety-tab is still in place, otherwise, you may be baffled by your camcorder's refusal to do any recording!

Switch On

What happens next depends on the particular model: you may find that the machine goes automatically into record mode on switch-on, or you may have to press an additional button to ready it for recording. Either way, you will now have a picture of some kind in the viewfinder. This picture may be in monochrome, or it may be in colour if your machine is fitted with one of the new miniature LCD screens. These colour finders do give you an approximate rendering of the colours you are recording, but they tend to be of lower definition than the black-and-white types of finder. Because of this, manual focusing of the picture from the viewfinder image may be more difficult.

If the viewfinder picture is blurred and indistinct, check that the camera lens is correctly focused. Do this by switching to auto-focus, and then aim the camcorder at some suitable object. If the viewfinder image is still not sharp, you should now check that the eyepiece diopter adjustment is correct for your eyesight: you will find the adjustment ring or knob for this near to the eyepiece.

On-off control of the camcorder is simplicity itself. You will find the camera button located close to the hand-grip on the right hand side of the body. Usually, it is positioned so that it can be operated by the thumb, and normally one press is needed to start recording and a second press to stop.

Just above the camera button, you will almost certainly find two more. These are buttons which operate the power-zoom on the lens, and they should be comfortably accessible to the first and second fingers of the right hand, although different models vary on this. So, now is a good time to try out the zoom controls while watching the effect in the viewfinder.

Test Shots

This done, you are almost ready to take your first shots on video, but before you do, check first that you have the correct white balance setting for the lighting conditions so that the recording will be made with the true colour values. This is necessary because the light in, say, an artificially lit room is warmer in tone than daylight outside, even on a brilliantly sunny day. Your eye makes a natural adjustment for this when looking at the scene direct so that the colour appears the same irrespective of the lighting. Camcorders on the other hand have to be given a little help to cope with different kinds of lighting by adjustment of their internal white balance settings to enable them to 'see' white as the same neutral colour regardless of the conditions.

Setting the white balance used to be a fiddly and time-consuming procedure, but nowadays it is done automatically, or by setting presets, or manually by aiming the camcorder at a standard white reference. Unless you are on auto white balance, check the settings each time you move outdoors or come back indoors.

Now you can begin to take some test shots. First, get used to the correct way of holding the machine. Slip your right hand through the hand grip strap and adjust it for comfort if necessary. Then position your right thumb over the camera button, and rest your index and second fingers just clear of the zoom switches.

Raise the camcorder and rest it against your face so that the viewfinder picture can be clearly seen, bringing up your left hand to provide additional steadying underneath the camcorder body at the lens end.

Now take a few shots to get used to the camera control, having first set everything to auto. Press the button gently but firmly and without jerking the camcorder each time you start and stop.

Next, switch from autofocus to manual and practise setting the focus by hand while you watch the effect in the viewfinder. Even though you will probably normally use autofocus, there will be times when you need to use manual. Using the fingertips of the left hand, gently turn the focus ring (being careful to keep clear of the leans itself) or actuate the focus control as appropriate.

Zooming the Lens

Try the effect of zooming the lens, first to wide angle and then to telephoto, adjusting the focus in and out on each of these two extreme settings. You will discover that it is much easier to find the exact point of focus when the zoom is set to telephoto, partly due to the enlargement of the image and partly to the fact that the focus depth of field is much shallower at this end of the zoom. This is a useful aid to accurate manual focusing: zoom in to tele-photo, set the focus, and then zoom back out to frame the shot the way you want it. For this, you can use either the power zoom buttons (right hand), or the manual zoom lever on the lens barrel (left hand), if fitted.

While you are experimenting with the zoom, note how much easier it is to hold the picture in the viewfinder steady when it is set to wide-angle. Close-ups taken on telephoto are often so shaky as to be unwatchable, so take the hint and keep to the wide angle end of the zoom for most of your shooting. If your lens has a macro setting for shooting big close-ups of small subjects, you could also experiment with this.

Many camcorders are provided with a means of manually overriding the automatic exposure control setting. Auto-exposure controls work by taking an average reading of the brightness of the

Above: The left hand provides steadying and operates the manual focus and zoom controls as well as the other camera buttons on both compact and shoulder-mount models.

Left: Most of the weight of compact camcorders is supported by the right hand on the hand-grip leaving the fingers and thumb clear to operate the on-off and power-zoom buttons.

subject and setting the exposure to suit this average. This is fine in most cases, but there are times when averaging the exposure is less than ideal.

A common example of problems with auto-exposure is where you have a dark foreground subject, say a building, which has bright sky in the background. In photographic terms, this is called backlighting, and the camcorder's attempt to find a compromise setting generally results in the under-exposure of the foreground, though some machines have metering systems which are sufficiently sophisticated to avoid the worst effects of this.

To help you offset backlight under-exposure, your camcorder will probably provide some form of manual override, the commonest being the provision of a simple backlight button. When you press this, the exposure is increased by a fixed amount which lightens both the foreground subject and the background. However, some machines go one better than this by providing full manual control of the exposure to allow you to make a more precise correction while observing the effect on the image in the viewfinder. This override may even enable you to make full picture fades; alternatively, you may have the facility of a separate fade button which will fade both picture and sound simultaneously.

Finally on the subject of exposure, if your camcorder has a gain-up switch, you can use this if you are working in poor light to further increase the exposure electronically. Gain-up does tend to make the picture look rather grainy, though, so it is best to look on it as a last resort and reserve it for those times when a grainy picture is better than no picture at all.

If your camcorder is a two-speed machine, it will have an SP/LP selector switch which you should get into the habit of checking before you do any important recording. Also, you may have the high speed shutter feature. or even some form of program auto-exposure. Hopefully, you will have one very useful button: record review. This is a real time saver, because it automatically plays back the last few seconds of the previous shot as a check before returning you to record mode ready to take the next shot. Try it, and you'll quickly see what a boon record-review can be.

Replay

For normal playback over the viewfinder (or on a television screen), you will need to use the tape-running buttons, and these are generally grouped separately from the camera controls. There are buttons for 'play', 'stop', 'rewind', and so on, just like the ones on a table-top video recorder. Buttons for 'audio dub' and 'insert', if these are facilities on your model, are often in this group, together with a camera/VTR button to switch you from camera controls to tape playback controls as required.

By now, you should be starting to see some interesting results

Below: A comprehensive display of signals and indicators which enable the operator to monitor the 'camera' functions through the viewfinder while recording is in progress. Included are warnings for low battery, tape end and condensation ('dew'), together with date/time indicators which can be switched off if desired. The 'shutter' signal indicates when the High Speed Shutter is on, and the cursor-type indicator above it shows the brightness of the scene being recorded and hence the lens aperture as set by the automatic exposure system. The two signals above the viewfinder show the camcorder record-mode and the White Balance mode setting.

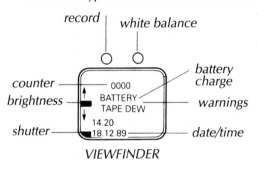

warnings

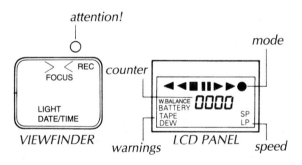

Above: An alternative signals configuration in which the display is split between the view-finder, which includes the autofocus status, low light warning and record on/off, and a separate LCD panel mounted elsewhere on the camcorder body. In this typical example, the 'attention!' signal draws the operator's notice to the LCD panel where the specific condition is indicated. The panel also shows the camcorder speed setting (SP or LP), and the tape running modes, ie play, stop, record, fast forward etc.

on your first tape even if they are just pot-shots taken at random. You will also have noticed that the viewfinder is displaying signal indications as well as the picture itself. There may also be a panel on the side of the camcorder with an LCD display giving additional information. The extent of these signal displays depends on the model, but with the help of the instruction book you will gradually learn to recognise what the signals mean and how they can help you to operate the camcorder to its best advantage.

'Battery', for instance, is a warning that you have only a minute or so of battery-time left before you will have to stop the shoot to allow the battery to be changed or recharged. 'Light' is a warning to check that the exposure (as shown by the picture in the viewfinder) is adequate. A tape-counter readout in the finder is a very convenient way of finding your way around the recordings which are already on the tape, and there may be other indicators such as 'SP/LP' to remind you of the operating mode. Probably the most useful indicator on a shoot is the one which shows whether or not you are actually recording pictures – it's easy to forget whether you have just pressed the camera control on or off!

A Mini-movie

To continue with this practice shoot, move outdoors – if you are not there already – where there will be more light and plenty of room to work in. If you can take a member of the family with you to stand in as a practice subject, so much the better.

Switch the camcorder back to record mode, check the white balance and set the focus to auto so that you can concentrate all your attention on the picture. Perhaps you could begin by taking a wide-angle shot or two of the house and the garden, so set the zoom to wide angle and select your first shooting position. Frame the shot in the viewfinder, and gently press the camera button to start the shot while holding the picture steady.

After a run of say five or six seconds, press the button again to stop the machine on record-pause while you move to a new position for the next shot – this might include both the house and part of the garden. Line up the shot in the viewfinder as before,

First Outdoor Shoot – Recap

1 Check battery is fully charged, fit and switch on.
2 Load tape cassette.
3 Switch to record; check picture in viewfinder.
4 Check focus (manual or automatic).
5 Check eye-piece adjustment.
6 Check correct white balance.
7 Raise camcorder and hold in comfortable position.
8 Select first shooting position.
9 Frame shot in view-finder, preferably with zoom on wide-angle.
10 Press camera button ON and hold picture steady.
11 After 5–6 seconds press camera button OFF and stop machine on record-pause.
12 Move to new position and repeat from 10 as many times as you like, starting a new shot for each new subject.

press the camera button again and away you go on shot two, still keeping the camcorder as steady as you can.

Having learned to hold the camcorder still for these static scenes, and having resisted all temptations to pan the camcorder to and fro to 'get it all in' you can now move in for some closer shots. These could show some activity going on in the garden – someone weeding a flowerbed, say, or children playing in the sand-pit.

Hold the camcorder to one subject at a time, starting a new shot every time you change to a new subject; each of these shots could be of say five to ten seconds duration. This time, because your subjects are not static objects but people, you can move the camera as necessary to keep them in the centre of the frame – but stay with the subject, don't pan part-way through to show something else. Don't zoom the lens in and out, either, but save this effect for the last shot in which you zoom out to a wide view of the garden again.

Having exhausted the pictorial possibilities and/or the patience of your subjects, switch from record-pause to stop and then to the tape-running controls. Rewind the tape back to the beginning and do a replay of the shots you have just taken. The odds are that you will be delighted with the results of this simple little shoot, particularly if you have managed to avoid the besetting sin of most first-time camcorder users, that is of panning the camera in an aimless fashion over everything in sight.

When you later screen a second replay on your colour television, it's likely that you will be even more pleased with your efforts: the colours, the movement, the thrill of seeing and hearing the sights and sounds of the place where you live and of the people who live there; it's all magic, and a moment to be savoured.

If your camcorder has twin speeds, it might be a good idea to repeat the exercise at the LP speed, assuming the first recording was done at standard speed. Comparison of the two recordings will then give you an indication of the difference in quality between the two.

At first glance, you may not notice any obvious differences, but if you look more closely you may spot a slight increase in the graininess of the picture at the LP speed, especially in the darker areas if you were shooting in poor light. Also, the vertical edges of objects such a fence-posts may be slightly fuzzy, an effect which is more pronounced if the edges contrast strongly with the background.

You will also see a difference between the two recording speeds when you play back in slow-motion or still-frame. Paradoxically, LP often fares better than SP under these conditions because the noise-bar interference on the pictures tends to be less for LP. However, camcorders vary considerably in this respect, and many of the newer ones give virtually disturbance-free pictures at any playback speed.

Here ends your first video shoot. Although you could re-use the tape for another recording, you may decide to keep it: it's surprising how even the most unambitious personal video recordings often contains scenes, or just brief moments, which are worth preserving. If so, now might be a good time to remove the safety-tab from the cassette to avoid the risk of accidental erasure.

Finally, if you ended your camcorder Day One with the 'battery' warning flashing in the viewfinder, you will need to recharge it to be ready for Day Two. Note though that, in spite of the warning, the battery will not be quite fully discharged: the warning comes on a little early to ensure that the camcorder is still able to eject the cassette before it shuts down completely. If the battery is recharged in this state, it will gradually lose its capacity to recharge fully due to what is called the 'memory effect'. To avoid this, it should be fully discharged once in every few recharge cycles. Special dischargers, which are available via mail order, should be used to carry this out properly, without harm to the battery. Some chargers have a facility which automates the whole recharging process.

3 Day Two: your first location shoot

Having taken your first steps on the road to becoming a video movie maker, you can now begin to run a little. Already, the basics of camcorder operation are becoming routine, and any initial uncertainties over how to cope with so many different control buttons are evaporating. In fact, camcorders are not only very simple to use – they're fun.

Why not turn your next video shoot into a day out with the family or friends? A zoo, park, or some other attractive open-air venue will provide you with lots of photographic opportunities while keeping other members of the party happily occupied. At this early stage in your video career, don't worry too much about making a complete record of the day. More ambitious projects will be possible when you have become fully proficient with your new equipment. For now, use the occasion as a means of learning more of the essential techniques which you will need later to produce first-rate movies.

Steady Shots

Take the question of stance, for instance. Although you have already learned how to hold the camcorder, the way that you stand while you are holding it is important too. Ideally, of course, the best support for any kind of camera is to mount it on a tripod, but tripods are awkward things to carry and they also have a dampening effect on spontaneity.

The trick, therefore, is to make your body imitate a tripod – as far as that is possible with two legs instead of three. So, with the

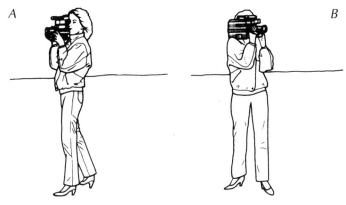

(a) The correct way to stand while holding a camcorder if no additional support is available; (b) shows how to 'pre-swing' before starting to take a pan-shot. (c) lean against walls, trees or whatever is available; (d) rest your elbows on car-roofs or low walls for extra steadiness.

camcorder firmly held in both hands and braced lightly against the forehead, stand with your feet slightly apart and your elbows tucked firmly into your sides... and relax.

If there's a handy tree, wall or fence to provide the third leg, rest against it: this will increase your camera steadiness quite dramatically. On the street, the roof of your car may be at just the right height for you to rest your elbows as you take the shot, and there are all sorts of other items of street furniture such as lamp-posts which can serve as props.

Panning and Tilting

Panning the camcorder, that is swinging it round through a horizontal arc, is a camera movement often used to excess by amateurs. Nevertheless, it has its place in camcorder operating techniques and there is a right way of doing it which is worth learning and practising.

To pan a camcorder smoothly, hold it normally while rotating your body from the hips to mimic the action of a pan-and-tilt head on a tripod. The snag to this is that although a pan-head can rotate through a full circle, your hips are limited to about a quarter of this movement. For this reason, it is best to practise a pan before you shoot, starting with body pre-swung through half of the movement in the opposite direction – rather like winding up a spring. This way, you will begin the pan smoothly and avoid running out of body-swing before you reach the end.

For more information on when to pan and when not to, see Chapter 6. For now, continue to hold the camcorder steadily except to follow the subject as you did on Day One. Above all, resist the temptation to pan the camcorder back and forth, this terrible technique is known as hosepiping and will ruin any shot.

Helpline

Question
Bright background causes the auto-iris to reduce exposure and foreground objects become featureless silhouettes. How can this be overcome?

Answer
Reframe the shot to exclude bright background, or
Correct for backlight by pressing backlight button or by
making manual adjustments to the iris (depending on model).

Tilting is the vertical equivalent of panning, and similar rules apply. In addition, tilt-shots have to be taken with extra caution because of the problem of backlight (see page 29). Suppose you are taking a shot of something tall such as a giraffe. If you want to get in close enough to see the detail of his beautiful body markings, you won't be able to include much of his neck which will be mostly sticking out through the top of the frame. Naturally, therefore, you will want to tilt the camcorder right up to the head, but if the shot now includes a large area of bright sky in the background, the auto-iris will reduce the exposure and George's head will become a featureless silhouette.

More on backlight

To save the shot, you can do one of two things: reframe the shot to exclude the sky, perhaps by moving to an angle where the sky is obscured by a building; or, correct for the backlight either by pressing the backlight button or by making a manual adjustment to the iris (depending on which facility is provided on your machine). The improvement will immediately show up in the viewfinder as the detail in the foreground lightens and becomes visible again; however, the sky in the background will also lighten, and perhaps even become over-exposed if there are some particularly bright clouds in the shot.

Another snag is that correcting backlight while carrying out a tilt is rather tricky. A better solution is to split the take into two shots, the first (pre-tilt) one being exposed normally, and the second (tilted) one being given the correction. Some of the newer camcorders apply automatic correction for backlight without need for any button-pushing, so tilts or pans into backlight can be successfully undertaken without spoiling the shot.

If you are shooting video in a zoo where animals are kept behind bars, you are likely to come up against situations which prove that auto-focus systems are not quite as clever as you are. As with any automatic system, it is the unusual situation which can cause a problem, and here the problem is that most AF systems tend to focus on the cage bars in the foreground rather than on the animal lurking behind them – or the focus may hunt nervously from one to the other. The solution, of course, is to switch to manual and do the job yourself, using the 'zoom in to telephoto' routine (see page 28).

As you wander round with your camcorder, you may well encounter significant changes in the character of the light during the course of a day's shoot. Not only may the strength of the light vary, perhaps from full sunshine to overcast, but the colour of the light can also change. Even on a cloudless, sunny day, the late afternoon sunlight is much warmer in tone than it is at noon. If your viewfinder picture is not in colour, you have to rely on your camcorder's white balance system to get the colour-balancing right for you – and it probably will.

However, it makes sense to keep the variations of lighting within reasonable bounds from shot to shot by shooting your scenes in groups which are consistently lit. If you happen to stray into an area of mixed day and artificial lighting, say at a window-table in a câfé, beware! The combination of warm and cold light can produce strange colour effects and the white balance setting becomes a compromise which may produce less than satisfactory results. Since you are still in the process of learning about your camcorder's capabilities, it might be a good idea to deliberately try some of these mixed light shots and to shoot comparisons between fully auto white balance and outdoor/indoor presets, if your machine gives you this choice of operation.

Storylines

On Day One, the simple exercise of shooting a few scenes in the garden was partly to familiarise you with the idea of editing in camera. As you recorded each shot, each shot-change was an edit, and the order in which the scenes are viewed on playback was decided by the order in which they were taken. This is quite unlike the situation when you shoot still photographs because these can be viewed in any order.

Although this may seem to be a statement of the obvious, it is in fact a very important point which goes to the very roots of movie making. As shot follows shot on the screen, your viewers will instinctively relate each to what has gone before in order to construct a thread of story – even if this story is as rudimentary as 'first we saw A, and then we saw B'. So it is kinder to your audience if your shots follow a logical progression. Keep interruptions to the smooth flow of the images to a minimum by eliminating false starts and shots which don't belong within a particular group.

Tidy beginnings and endings to shots are important. Decide what each shot is going to include and get it properly focused and framed before you press the button. There is nothing worse then sitting through shots which wobble around and zoom in and out while the camcorder operator is getting things sorted out. If you do find that you have recorded an unsatisfactory shot, cut your losses there and then by reversing back to the beginning so that you can over-record with something better before continuing with the rest of the shoot. If you leave the dud shot in place you are stuck with it, and you will dislike it more and more each time you replay the tape.

Backspace time

Bear in mind, when you are starting a shot, that you should allow for the backspace time. If you have an ordinary video recorder which does not have 'backspace' or 'fine edit', you will probably have noticed, when changing from one recording to the next, that for a while the picture is spoilt by various forms of disturbance that take several seconds to clear. This is because the electronic pulses which control the scanning of the video picture are interrupted at the point of the change, and the system takes quite a time to re-adjust itself.

This is all taken care of on camcorders. At the beginning of each new shot, the tape first back-tracks over the last few seconds of the previous recording, after which it reverses and returns back to the edit-point during which the camcorder's electronics find and lock onto the previously recorded control-pulses. As it reaches the end of these, it automatically switches into record mode and the new shot begins to go onto the tape.

In practice, therefore, when you press the camera button there is a delay of about one second before the camcorder actually begins to record anything. In many cases, this delayed start will not be noticeable, especially if there is no important action right at the beginning; the only real effect is that the shot is about one second shorter than you intended, and you will soon learn to allow for this by adding a second or so to the time before you press the button to end the shot.

Take extra care when a shot begins with a pan. It is good technique to allow a few seconds at the beginning of a shot before the pan movement actually starts to allow the audience time to take in the scene. If you forget to allow for the backspace time, you may find that this time margin has been reduced noticeably – the pan may even start before the backspacing is complete – and this will not look good on the screen.

If your camcorder has a record-review button, you will find this to be a most useful facility to have at your disposal when you are out on a shoot because it enables you to make a quick check on the last few seconds of the previous shot before starting to record the next. The manual alternative, in which you have to switch from record mode to play to find the end of the previous recording before returning to record mode, is messy, time-consuming and wasteful of precious battery-time. So if you have record-review, use it – and use the standby switch too if you have one: another battery saver.

Editing in camera

You may sometimes wish to shorten the end of the previous shot by over-recording it with the beginning of the next one. In this case, you have to go through the full manual routine as outlined above, stopping on play-pause and switching back to record-pause when you reach the desired edit-out point on the previous recording. This is, in fact, real editing in camera, and when you have become accustomed to the routine you will find that it makes all the difference between a good movie and one which is tedious and irritating to watch.

To take a typical example: you are at the zoo and have just recorded a very nice shot of a chimpanzee peeling and eating a banana. In the expectation of more amusing antics from the little chap, you keep the camcorder running on … and on … and on. Nothing much happens, and you eventually decide to cut. If you simply start the next shot from here, you are left with an awkward pause and this spoils the effect of what has gone before. Obviously, the thing to do is to return to the point where the eating of the banana comes to an end and begin the next shot from there.

Quite apart from achieving neat endings to actions, bear in mind that a shot has a natural length beyond which it should not run. As you gain experience, you will learn to sense the point at which to cut to a fresh shot from a new angle. Shot lengths are discussed more fully in Chapter 7. For now, resolve to hold your shots only for as long as is needed to allow the audience to take in the details of the scene or to cover interesting action.

Sound Checks

So far, we have been taking the sound recording very much for granted. Indeed, the odds are that if the pictures are looking good, the sound will also be recording satisfactorily and will at least be representative of the atmosphere at the particular location.

It is always a good policy, though, to check the sound as well as the pictures whenever possible. Many, but sadly not all, camcorders enable you to monitor the sound in the field via an earpiece which is plugged into a socket provided specially for this purpose. This enables you to maintain a continuous check on both the direct input off the microphone as well as of playback of the recorded sound, though the earpiece and its connecting cord can be something of a nuisance to wear all the time.

As you near the end of your first video safari, the low-battery warning in your viewfinder may begin to flash, indicating that you have not long to go before switch-off for the day. If you have yet to record a scene which will end the tape in a suitable way – maybe a farewell wide shot of the whole park, or of people beginning to pack up and go home – now is the time to do it before the battery goes completely and the camcorder switches itself off. If you miss out on shooting a closing shot because of this, the recording will seem to end rather abruptly. Some people take a fully charged spare battery along with them just in case!

Checklist

These stylistic refinements will add a professional touch to your video:

- *Hold the camcorder firmly; stand with the feet slightly apart and the elbows tucked into the body.*
- *Rehearse important pan shots. Remember to pre-swing before starting to shoot – no hose-piping.*
- *Beware of backlight problems on an upward tilt.*
- *Switch to manual focus where necessary.*
- *Maintain consistent lighting for sequences of shots.*
- *Maintain a logical sequence of events – a storyline.*
- *Edit in camera – give your shots tidy beginnings and endings.*
- *Frame and focus your shots before you shoot.*
- *Allow for backspace at the start of each shot.*
- *Know when to close a shot.*
- *Use record/review to conserve battery power.*
- *Use an earpiece or headphones to monitor the sound.*
- *Allow battery time for a concluding shot.*

Learning by looking at your first results

B ack at home after your first location-shoot – at the zoo or wherever – and having viewed your efforts in glorious colour, you will perhaps be asking yourself, 'What next?' Well, with a camcorder, the world is very much your oyster, and the possibilities are limitless. However, before you sally forth on your next video shoot, take a long, cool look at your first tape to identify any mistakes you may have made so that you can avoid them next time.

When the initial excitement has subsided, settle down on your own for a closer and more critical showing. Try to view your work as dispassionately as you would any other programme you might watch on the television – but don't be too hard on yourself, you are now comparing your efforts with the work of skilled professionals!

Wobbly Shots

Wobbly shots are the hall-mark of the raw amateur. The professional photography we see on television is shot from camera tripods except for some newsreel material – and even hand-held news shots are almost as steady when the camcorder is being operated by an experienced cameraman.

So, if you find that too many of your shots come into the wobbly category, resolve to do better next time by concentrating on getting this basic technique right. You don't even need to shoot any video to practise this: simply switch to 'rehearsal' or 'monitor' mode, and work at keeping the image in the viewfinder as steady as you can. Maybe you were tempted to take hand-held shots on telephoto – perhaps with a very good reason, lions in a safari park are not very approachable and often the only way to shoot them in close-up is with a long-focus lens. On the other hand, shaky close-ups, even of magnificent beasts, are not very good to watch and you really need to provide yourself with additional means to help you hold the picture steady. If your camcorder doesn't have an image stabiliser and you decide that a tripod is the answer, you will find a selection of these to choose from at your local photographic dealers. Ask to see the ones which are specially made for video cameras. These have sturdy telescopic aluminium legs which are well braced to provide good support, and are fitted with pan-and-tilt heads to enable you to make smooth camera moves. Heads designed with a fluid-type action are the smoothest of all.

Unfortunately, it has to be admitted that tripods are heavy and bulky things to carry round, and you might consider the use of a mini-tripod (which can be supported on wall-tops), a chest-pod or a monopod. These do not have the sophisticated pan-and-tilt heads of the full tripod, so they are not the complete answer. If you can afford such luxuries, the device known as the Steadicam JR will give you perfectly smooth shooting even while you are walking your camcorder through a tracking shot!

Autofocus Systems

If you have been shooting with the help of autofocus, you should have few problems with regard to image sharpness. If one or two of your shots are less sharp than they might be, it may be because the conditions did not suit your particular autofocus (AF) system.

AF systems are of two main types: optical, and infra-red. Optical systems use the actual picture image as the signal source which is continuously evaluated electronically as a means of determining and holding the point of focus. These optical systems work well, though the accuracy falls off in poor light and when the subject is dark in tone or lacking in contrast.

The alternative infra-red system uses a beam which is emitted from the camcorder and reflected back off the subject, the time

HELPLINE

Here are some answers to solve the technical hitches you may have had with your first movie:

Question: Why are some of the shots shaky?
Answer: Perhaps you had the camcorder lens set to telephoto. Move closer to your subjects and use a wider angle. If shake is still a problem, use a camcorder with an image stabiliser – or buy a tripod.

Question: Why are some of the shots out of focus?
Answer: The type of subject, or poor light, may have prevented the autofocus from operating properly. Use manual focus for problem shots.

Question: Why are some shots dark and muddy?
Answer: There may have been a backlight problem (see page 29), or perhaps the lighting at the scene itself was too drab. Check the picture in the viewfinder before taking the shot.

Question: How can burn-out on bright, highlighted subjects be avoided?
Answer: Angle the shot so the light comes cross-wise at the subject, or reduce the proportion of dark background areas relative to the subject.

Question: How can graininess on plain surfaces with bright primary colours be avoided?
Answer: Steer clear of these subjects. The effect results from technical limitations in the video equipment. Less of a problem on high band formats.

Question: Wind, traffic or camcorder noise have drowned out the required soundtrack. How can this be avoided?
Answer: Use an extension microphone, preferably a unidirectional type, aimed away from the unwanted noise.

taken for the reflection to return being measured and converted to a distance setting. Infra-red systems work in any light and on most types of subject, but accuracy reduces with distance and with subjects which reflects poorly.

Both types of system can be confused by reflections off glass and other shiny surfaces, and they can be beaten by rapidly moving subjects although the speed at which the newer systems work is incredibly fast. The technology, in fact, is getting better all the time: some AFs are now capable of holding the focus all the way from the front surface of the lens to infinity and will lock onto the subject even if it moves from centre-screen right to the edge of the frame.

Natural Light

Maybe some of your pictures are rather dark and muddy-looking. One cause of this is the problem of backlighting. If this seems to be the cause, resolve in future to spot the effect in your camcorder viewfinder before you press the button so that you can take the necessary action to avoid the fault.

However, backlight may not in fact be the culprit. The scene itself may have been unsatisfactory as a subject, with flat lighting and dull colours combining to produce the sad-looking picture you see on the screen. Again, the viewfinder image will alert you to the problem by showing you how the camcorder is seeing the scene. So get into the habit of really looking at the viewfinder picture as you line up the shot. If this scrutiny raises doubts in your mind, move on and find a better subject.

The way that a scene is lit is important: in general, the best lighting for outdoor video is slightly hazy sunshine coming at an angle from behind the camera. In such a situation, the colours show up the best advantage, and the angling of the light helps to 'model' the detail and separate the planes to increase the illusion of depth. For close-ups of people's faces, hazy, rather than full, sun gives sufficient modelling but without casting unflattering heavy shadows; it also reduces problems with glare reflected off light-coloured clothing and other surfaces.

Camcorder microphones are vulnerable to wind noise. One solution is to use an assistant to provide shelter if this becomes a problem.

If the day is overcast, where possible shoot with whatever light there is behind you as this will maximise the exposure and help prevent the colours from becoming washed-out and muddy. If you are getting a 'low light' warning in the viewfinder, take a careful look at the picture before giving up on the shot; if the light is only marginally below par it may still be worth taking despite the warning. In really dark conditions, and where a poor shot is preferable to none at all, use the gain-up switch (if you have one) and accept the picture may be grainy.

Contrast

Photographically speaking, contrast is one of the elements in the making of a good picture. Unfortunately, video imaging systems are not very tolerant of contrast, and the range of brightness between the lightest and darkest areas of a picture which can be reproduced is very much less for video than it is for ordinary colour photography.

So, if you are taking shots of people in brilliant sunshine, be wary of shots which include areas of white set against dark backgrounds. If the day is hot and foreheads are glistening, these shiny surfaces will 'burn out' in a most unbecoming way when you play back the shot unless you take steps to prevent this from happening. One way is to change the angle of the shot so that the light comes cross-wise and hence will not be reflected straight back to the camera. Another is to reduce the proportion of dark background area relative to the subject, either by shifting to a more suitable setting or by moving in to a bigger close-up so that the dark background is reduced in size. The symptoms of over-contrast are not always easy to spot on a monochrome viewfinder picture, so it pays to be specially vigilant if the light is very bright.

Another video weakness to guard against is the coarse and grainy look of plain surfaces in bright primary colours, especially reds. Shiny plastic rainwear and children's toys are common examples. Yet another irritating picture defect is the flickering moiré effect which is often seen on finely-patterned surfaces such as the stripes in men's suits. These picture faults are due to the technical compromises which are built into video and television systems. Unless you are fortunate enough to possess a high band camcorder in which these defects have been designed out, the solution is to steer clear of such subjects. Remember that these are colour effects, and they will therefore not show up on a black and white viewfinder.

Flying Erase

As you play back your shots, you may notice colour disturbance at some of the picture edits – unless, that is, your machine has the feature known as flying erase. Flying erase is a system in which the erase heads are located, not in a fixed position, but mounted instead on the rotating head-drum alongside the video heads. The gap between the two sets of heads is thus virtually nil, and so the tape is cleared of all previously recorded signals before it reaches the record-heads. Hence, colour disturbances due to the over-recording of unerased signals, which occurs on machines with the older fixed erase heads, is eliminated. More and more camcorders are coming off the production lines with this useful feature; however, it is not a point which need concern you unduly if you happen to have one of the older machines, as the effect is notice-able only on edits where there is a big change in the character of the colours at the shot-change.

Sound Problems

Let's turn now to some problems you may have encountered on your sound recordings. Camcorder microphones are contrary devices: sometimes they fail to pick up the sounds that they should, and sometimes they hear things that they shouldn't.

Unlike light, which can reach the lens from sources far beyond our galaxy, sound is a very localised phenomenon. Its ability to travel over distance is limited, and it is therefore a commodity which the recordist has to reach for. The best place to position a microphone is always as close as possible to the source of the sound.

Unfortunately, the right position for taking the picture is seldom ideal for picking up the sound, especially when speech is being recorded, so on-board camcorder microphones do have their limitations. It will no doubt do a first-rate job of picking up the general sound atmosphere, or ambience of a scene. Outdoors, however, it is vulnerable to wind noise, especially if the shot is being taken right into the weather. It doesn't need to be a strong wind to ruin the sound on a shot, the lightest of breezes can sound like a Force 8 gale in spite of the foam wind-shield with which the microphone is no doubt adorned.

It can be very upsetting to have good shots spoiled in this way; once the noise is on the tape there's not much you can do about it except dub it out with a substitute background sound (see page 97). Prevention is better than cure, and the sensible thing to do is to physically shield the mike, either by angling the shot out of the wind, or by getting an assistant to shelter it bodily. Some camcorders have an electronic 'wind filter', a device which can be switched in to reduce wind noise.

Traffic noise is another enemy of the sound recordist. It is less of a problem if the camcorder microphone is a unidirectional type, that is one which tend to accept sound which is coming mainly from the camera direction. Loud noise from passing vehicles is doubly unwelcome because, not only does it drown out the wanted sound, but it also causes the camcorder's automatic gain control to lower the recording level; this generally takes some seconds to return to normal after the disturbance, during which time the wanted sound is not recorded properly.

'Audio nasties' can get onto the tape from sources which are much nearer to home than wind or passing traffic. The various whirrings and whinings which may be emitted by the camcorder itself, not to mention any noises which you make while operating the controls, are liable to be faithfully picked up by the on-board microphone. Some camcorders – and some operators – are much quieter than others, and the problem only becomes acute when you are recording indoors under quiet conditions; outdoors, these unwanted sounds tend to be lost in the general background.

Extension microphones

The answer to the three problems of wind, traffic and camcorder noise is to be found in the use of an extension microphone: it can be more easily sheltered from the wind, it can be a super-directional type if need be and so help to exclude the sound of passing traffic, and it can be placed far enough away to reduce camera handling noises to zero.

With a microphone on a long lead plugged in, the on-board mike is automatically disconnected and the sound can then be picked up at much closer range. For more advice on how to go about selecting and using an extension microphone, see Chapter 10.

If this seems like a catalogue of disaster, don't be discouraged: you are unlikely to have hit all these problems on your first outing, but forewarned is forearmed. Now that you are aware of the possible technical snags, you can make sure you avoid them in future.

Perhaps some of your problems are not technical so much as aesthetic. Have you the feeling, perhaps, that the order of your shots is aimless and unsatisfying? Is it that some of your shots do not look as pictorially attractive as they might? If so, read on.

Indoor recording skills – Christmas festivities

I t's party time, and you and your camcorder are invited! Parties and camcorders do seem to go well together, and it's not difficult to think of reasons why.

Any really good party is a chaotic jumble of noise and movement, so you have vision and sound built in. It's a way of bringing together and mixing people, with lots of opportunities for candid camera shots of folk with their everyday guards down. It's also often an ideal time to update the family picture archive against the background of a happening which is in itself worth recording.

Parties can be set indoors or outdoors – or be split between the two. Each location has its video advantages and disadvantages. Outdoors, there is space, but there may be problems with light if the occasion is held during hours of darkness as well as uncertainties about the weather. Indoors, everything is under more control and camcorder operations can be pre-planned to a greater extent, particularly if the location is in your own home or some other familiar setting. The question of lighting can be sorted out in advance: ideally, in the interests of spontaneity, the normal lighting, whether artificial or daylight, will be adequate or can be supplemented without too much fuss.

Indoors, power supplies are generally on hand, and the camcorder can be run either directly off the mains via its adapter or on the battery which can easily be recharged between times. In fact, there are only two real disadvantages to indoor video filming. The first is that there is less room in which to work, and the second that the boomy quality of some interiors can make the recording of clear sound difficult. Camcorder operating noise can also be more of a problem.

While a simple one-off party can be a rewarding subject for video, Christmas parties, and in particular children's Christmas parties, offer even greater scope for creative video because they take place within the context of a whole season of festivity which has a built in story of its own.

Telling a Story

The idea of telling a story is important to discuss at this point, because it contains the secret of all good video. This is true whether the story is an epic with a cast of thousands or nothing more elaborate than a simple family situation. The story of a children's Christmas, climaxing in a party, comes towards the lower end of these two extremes, and we are going to take it as the plot on which can be built an interesting home video.

What, in video terms, is the story of a family Christmas? It is not simply one of scenes showing children excitedly unwrapping and playing with their new presents – or of shots taken at the party later in the day. Certainly, these are important highlights and should be given their proper place and emphasis in the narrative. However, you should not forget that there are low-key happenings which can also make excellent video and help in building up to the climaxes. So, while there is no need to spoil the fun by trying to make an overblown production out of your Christmas video, why not give a little time and thought to ways of showing the excitement leading up to the day itself.

Thinking in sequences

One of the advantages of shooting a video like this one is that the events group themselves quite naturally into sequences which advance the story in a way which your audience will have no difficulty in following. All you have to do is to go with the flow of events, letting each scene add to what has gone before. In fact, the trick that you need to learn to help you with this and all other movie making is to 'think in sequences'. What this means is simply that each time you line up a shot in the viewfinder and before you press the button, you should look on it not as an individual shot as you would a still photograph but as one of a group of shots. Ask yourself two questions:

☆ Does the shot fit in with the last one?
☆ Does the shot form part of a logical progression within the group?

If this sounds too complicated, don't be put off. Thinking in sequences is a mental trick that comes with practice, and some of the more advanced sequence building rules will be discussed in Chapters 6 and 8 when we come to consider post-production video editing techniques. For now, let's begin by jotting down a few ideas for sequences to make a Christmas movie which we will assume is being recorded in the final shot order, in other words, edited in camera.

Much of the thrill of Christmas lies in its anticipation. There is the bustle of the shopping centres with their decorated window displays and coloured lights; the traditional ritual of writing to Santa Claus; the visit to 'Santa' in a big city department store; the decoration of the Christmas Tree; and all kinds of other activities, including those in the kitchen to prepare the party food. On the day itself, there is not only the opening of the presents, and the party, but also the aftermath when it's all over to provide a fitting finale to the day's activities.

City lights

If you have decided on this as your opening sequence, you may like the idea of beginning it with a fade in on a close-up of some brightly lit seasonal decoration in a shopping precinct – the face of a life-size Santa would be an ideal way to set the mood. If your camcorder has a titling facility, you could even superimpose a title over this shot.

This could be followed by a wider shot to take in the overall scene, showing the dazzling displays and hurrying shoppers. This will establish the character of the location in the minds of the viewers. Then, you could continue with a whole succession of closer shots concentrating on the colour and glitter of shop windows in which the reflections of shoppers add their own element of movement and interest.

In an atmospheric kind of sequence like this, you should keep your shots fairly short, pulling back to a wider shot once in a while to provide extra visual variety and to re-establish the scene. Don't overdo the length of the sequence; two or three minutes should be ample as an opener for your movie.

You can have a lot of fun shooting city lights, but there are one or two points to watch out for if you are going to come away with some really effective footage. Remember that even if the precinct appears brightly lit to the eye, your camcorder will probably be working flat out to expose for the wide shots. The brightest objects are of course the lights themselves, but wide shots also include the darker areas which reduce the average brightness of the scene. The lens aperture will probably be working fully open, and this may over-expose the lights which will then tend to flare.

When you are shooting night-scenes such as these, avoid shots such as decorative street lights against a dark sky. These can be disappointing because the camcorder's auto-exposure system, in opening up the lens aperture to maximise the average brightness of the shot, will probably record the coloured lights as colourless points of light. If your camcorder has manual exposure control though, you can aim to expose for the lights and let the background take care of itself. A more accurate method, if you have the 'exposure lock' facility, is to zoom in on the lights, let the camcorder set the exposure on auto, and then lock this setting before zooming out back to the wide shot.

Focus can be more critical at lower lighting levels, and your autofocus system may be confused by reflections off the shop windows. If you have to resort to manual focusing, remember to

Decorating the Christmas tree: close the curtains to exclude day-light, and pick a camera position which gives a good wide-angle view and also allows close-ups of the tree and its decorators.

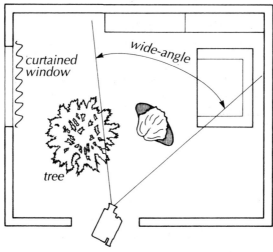

The party: choose a fixed camera position with as clear a field of view as possible if you are shooting from a tripod and using an extension microphone. Otherwise, you could use a mobile camera, but curtain the window if there is risk of backlight or mixed light problems.

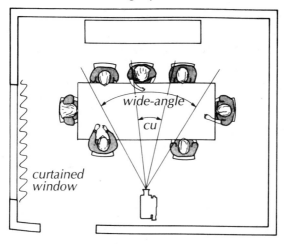

use the telephoto focusing routine (see page 28) to help you get your shots nice and sharp.

At the end of the sequence, you may choose to close it with a fade out, but a straight cut to the first shot of the next sequence might be more brisk and businesslike. If the next sequence is to be 'Letters to Santa', in fact, you could cut from a repeat of the original close-up of the Santa's head to a close-up of a letter already headed 'Dear Santa'... This is what thinking in sequences is all about!

Letters to Santa

In contrast to the first sequence, the keynote here is one of simplicity and naturalness. Even so, if the sequence is to come off it will have to be stage-managed to some extent: children who are young enough to believe in Santa Claus are not old enough to carry the action on their own without the help of an adult to keep things moving. If the children are very young, the adult – mother, grandpa, or whoever – will have to do the writing, too.

To keep things as natural as possible, the scene should be shot in normal light, and one set-up worth considering is to place your subjects near to a window so that you can shoot in daylight. This has the added advantage of making a nice contrast to the night scenes in the previous sequence.

To make the most of the light coming through the window – which preferably should not be direct sunlight – seat the letter writers to face diagonally onto the window so that they are attractively cross-lit. The camcorder can then be operated from a position looking diagonally away from the window to face the subjects. Make sure none of the window area is included within the shot, otherwise you could be giving yourself a problem with backlighting.

A relatively static subject like this is best shot from off a tripod which would enable you to keep well back and work the zoom towards the telephoto end of the range for close-ups without risking spoiling your shots through camera-shake. This will perhaps help your younger performers to be less self-conscious, though you may find that the appearance of a tripod induces a fit of giggles in the cast. With a tripod you lose the freedom of camera mobility which you have with a hand-held camera, and if you decide to dispense with a tripod, a position at 3m (10ft) or so from the subjects will allow you to work the zoom from wide angle down to mid-range for close-ups.

Even with adult help, the attention span of small children is very short, so you will need to work quickly and grab any chances of good video as they happen. To follow the close-up of the pre-headed letter, the first shot should show all the performers together to establish them in the setting. To begin the action, the adult says something like: 'Now what shall we ask Santa to bring you for Christmas?' The rest of the scene is strictly *ad lib*!

As you shoot the scene, you have to tread a tight-rope, avoiding the fault of holding a shot too long if the action seems to have dried up, while simultaneously avoiding the opposite fault of cutting shots too short just before something begins to happen. However things turn out, try to reflect the mood of the scene by the pace of the cutting of your shots: if the children are quiet and thoughtful, the shots can be held a little longer than if they are lively and excited (provided that the adult does a good job of filling in the gaps in the action).

Each time you cut, use the interruption to give some stage directions without them being recorded onto the tape, but try to minimise the effect of jumps in the action by changing either the shot angle or size before you restart the recording. If you can, end the sequence with a pre-arranged payoff line. For example, the adult could say 'Well, Santa is certainly going to be busy!' Alternatively, you could let the recording run on, picking the best point at which to end it (and start recording the next sequence) later.

Decorating the tree

We are back to night scenes again. While the mood of the letters sequence was naturalistic, this time we can indulge in a little magic and mystery as we show the decking of the tree with all kinds of colourful lights and baubles. Once again, the principal performers could be children who are helping an adult. It is an interesting activity, so the chances are that they will quickly forget about the camcorder and behave naturally. Hence, the element of mystery has to be introduced in the way that the scene is shot and particularly in the way that it is lit. However, nothing very elaborate is called for, it's just a matter of putting the available lighting resources to the best possible use.

If your camcorder is one of the new low-light models which can take pictures down to levels of 2 lux, you could simply switch on the normal top lighting in your lounge and start recording some perfectly adequate pictures. For our present purpose, though, they would look rather flat and not very magical: try it and you'll probably agree. The trick is to augment this top light with more accented and directional lighting, so switch on a nearby standard or table lamp.

Immediately, the feel of the scene changes: the pool of light from the extra lamp creates its own little centre of colour and interest, and the flatness of the top lighting is relieved. With this as a starting point, you could go on to experiment with even more additional lights. If your lounge is equipped with batteries of spot-lamps and other sophisticated facilities, you could spend an hour or so trying out all kinds of variations before arriving at the best effect.

Great quantities of lighting wattage are not needed. The aim is to provide sufficient directional light to make the decorations sparkle, but they should be set against areas of soft shadow which will throw them into relief. If your camcorder has manual override of the exposure control, try the effect of this at various settings (with the camcorder picture shown on a colour television) so that you can work out the one which gives the best balance between the highlight and shadow areas.

To end your pre-shoot planning session, pick one or two camera positions which will keep you clear of all the coming and going. If you can, plan to use a tripod; with the camcorder firmly secured, you will then be able to zoom right in to fill the screen with individual baubles and still be placed to get good normal close-ups as well as wider shots of your performers absorbed in their task.

As a sequence, this simple little set-up holds great creative possibilities. You could, for instance, cut freely from close-up to close-up without the problems of jumps in the action which can spoil wider shots. This rather cinematic approach adds to the atmosphere of mystery and excitement. Remember, though, that the sound will also cut at each shot-change, so it's wise to make your in-camera picture cuts at times when no one is actually speaking.

As a climax, you could arrange for some of the room lights to be switched off one by one before the tree-lights are switched on for the first time (test them first). However, you really need exposure lock to make this effect work properly. Without it, the camcorder will try to compensate for the reduced light by increasing the exposure, and the picture will look muddy rather than magical. With exposure lock, you can set the exposure for the full lighting, and this setting is then unaffected both when the lamps are switched off and also when the tree-lights are switched on, thus giving the lit tree its full dramatic impact.

To complete the sequence, try for a few close-ups of the coloured light reflecting in the children's faces, after which a fade to black would bring the sequence to an appropriate close.

Opening the presents

This sequence is probably going to be shot very early in the morning, and it will take great strength of mind to get it all together. The results, however, can be well worth the effort, and it will all come that much easier if you have prepared things in advance.

At this hour, artificial light will be all the light there is, and your main job the night before will be to ensure that there is sufficient for your purposes. Fortunately, there is no need for anything very magical this time, ordinary top lighting should be perfectly adequate plus maybe one or two spot-lamps borrowed from the lounge. Children's bedrooms are usually small areas with light-coloured walls, so there should be enough reflected light to lighten up the main scene of action, but if you do bring in any additional low-level lighting, take care to position it where it will not get in the way of the camera or shine into the lens.

Present-opening sessions are generally unpredictable affairs, the pictures being shot with mobile camera on a catch-as-catch-can basis with the sound mostly consisting of the rustling of wrapping paper being undone and the excited squeaks of the recipients. Once again, the presence of an adult to help keep things going will make it easier for the cameraman, whose job it is to cover the most interesting bits of action wherever it may take place within the four walls of the room.

Although you may decide to begin with a fade in, the circumstances may leave you with insufficient time for these niceties, and a crash-in cut to the first shot probably set the mood for the sequence better in any case. With action as unpredictable as this is likely to be, and since you won't want to risk missing anything vital, you will probably opt for longish takes and let the mobility of the camera and the occasional zoom in or out provide the visual variety to help the sequence along.

If you can, end each take at an angle which excludes at least one of the parcel unwrappers from the frame. Then, you can begin the next shot with a close-up of that individual and so avoid the awkwardness of a jump in the action. For a final shot, pull back to a wider view of the scene and hold this for long enough to mark the winding-up of the sequence.

Kitchen preparations

Another change of scene, and with it another change of mood. The activities of the cook are the centre of attention, and the presence of children, spouse, dogs, cats or other subordinates are peripheral to the main action.

Kitchens are generally bright, well lit areas so there should be no exposure problems on that score except if there is mixed lighting, that is a mixture of daylight and artificial light, illuminating the scene. Daylight and ordinary tungsten light do not mix together very well photographically; on the other hand, fluorescent light is often used in kitchens and this mixes with daylight rather better than tungsten if 'daylight' tubes are in use, in which case set the camcorder white balance to the 'daylight' preset if you have the choice. Otherwise, auto white balance will probably cope adequately with mixed day/fluorescent.

Having ended the last sequence with a wide shot, it might be nice to begin this the same way to show Cook at work. Kitchens can be cramped, steamy places to swing a camcorder in, and if yours is particularly small you may want to use a wide-angle adapter-lens of the kind which screws onto the front of the lens to increase the angle of view. If you do use wide-angle, be careful not to come too close to your subject, as this can produce odd distortion effects.

With regard to content, the sequence can concentrate on various cooking activities, mostly in close-up and without the need for rigorous attention to continuity. Knives chopping carrots, spoons mixing in spices, rolling-pins rolling out the dough, bubbling pans ... there is lots of interesting and colourful action in a well run kitchen, enlivened now and again by the peering of children's eyes over the table-top at all that is going on. If you like, the whole sequence could be shot from their point of view.

The party

By this stage, you could be feeling that you are quite an old hand at Christmas video making; if so, recording the party should be child's play in every sense.

Shoot the party games sequence with a mobile camera and in available light if you can. The circumstances will dictate how much you can make of it from the standpoint of good video. The main job will probably boil down to making sure you have taken plenty of candid camera shots of those present, both adults and children.

If there is to be a sit-down meal, you will then have a much better opportunity to get some good shots, hopefully without missing out on too much of the turkey yourself. A main decision is whether to settle for one fixed camera position or whether to stay mobile. A fixed position allows the use of a tripod and, for the first time in this Christmas video shoot, the use of an extension micro-phone to enable you to make a good job of recording all those fascinating speeches that tend to be made after the second or third glass of wine. Try to arrange for attractive lighting; a few candles, for instance, can add a touch of distinction to the scene, and lounge spots can help to lighten the darker corners of the table.

Aftermath

This is intended as a sort of coda to the movie: fade in to scenes of rooms strewn with festive remains, stacked dishes awaiting washing up, some of the more senior party-goers taking a nap. Fade out.

These have been just a few ideas to get you started. There are lots of other ways of interpreting the theme, and the actual details will of course depend on your own Christmas story.

Camcorder holiday

Camcorders and holidays were made for each other. Think about all the video opportunities that await you: golden beaches, sparkling waves; the sound of the sea; snow-capped mountains, the swing of the ski-lift and the chatter of the wintersports crowds; sleepy Mediterranean villages; the tinkle of distant cowbells; the bustle of busy airports; the surge of city traffic. A whole world of colour and sound is waiting to be brought back on video tape, and camcorders are now so simple to operate, and so portable, that you can take pictures just about anywhere.

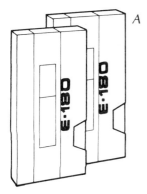

A

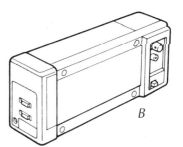

B

C

Here are three items to take with you when you go on holiday with your camcorder. A blank cassette – and maybe a spare – is an obvious essential (a), and you will certainly need to be able to recharge your camcorder battery as you go along, so don't forget to take your battery charger (b) with you. If you intend to record views of impressive scenery, it might be a good idea to take a tripod (c) along as well.

Holiday Equipment

What you pack apart from the camcorder itself depends on the kind of holiday you are planning and the amount of luggage you can reasonably handle. If you are travelling by car, carrying extra bits and pieces is less of a problem than if you are going by air. The additional equipment you will need with you on your holiday shoots will also depend on the importance that you – and your companions – attach to video making in relation to the other holiday activities. If the video is intended to be little more than shots of the folks taken as and when opportunity offers, you will obviously wish to be burdened with the barest minimum of tackle. If on the other hand the video is to be a record of a once in a lifetime trip, you are more likely to accept the need to go fully equipped and ready for all eventualities.

As far as minimum requirements go, you will need to take at least one blank video cassette with you. This is particularly necessary if you are using either the VHS-C or 8mm formats; unlike the ubiquitous standard VHS cassettes which can be bought just about anywhere, the availability of the mini-format cassettes tends to be patchy and you risk running out of tape at an awkward time.

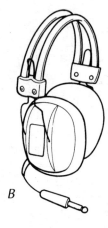

Here are some more items of 'holiday video' equipment. If your camcorder has an audio monitor socket, take an earpiece (a) or – preferably – a pair of headphones (b). An extension microphone (c) can also be worth considering when you are packing for the trip.

Check List

Remember to include these pieces of equipment in your holiday luggage:
- blank video cassette
- battery charger
- spare rechargeable battery

and if you have space:
- earpiece socket or fullsize headphones
- extension microphone
- tripod/mini-tripod
- bag in which to carry video gear

Battery charging

Another essential item to take with you is a battery charger; if you are really keen not to be caught with a flat battery, take a spare rechargeable battery too. Camcorders are rather power-hungry beasts and the average of forty minutes of recording time per charge seems to last no time at all when you are actually on a shoot – a spare battery can be a god-send. If you are likely to be using the camcorder near the car, it might be worth taking one of the special leads which enable you to feed power from the car battery directly to the camcorder; however, this is obviously not a practical option for general holiday use.

On the other hand, there are battery chargers which can be run off a car's lighter-socket, and this does open up possibilities for running camcorders at locations such as remote camp sites which do not have a public mains power supply. Otherwise, the way to keep your battery topped up is to use a mains charger. If you are holidaying in hotels, or in places such as caravan parks which provide electric power hook-ups, you should have no problem in this country or on the continent, provided that the plug on your charger fits the power supply socket or can be made to do so via an adapter.

However, many people these days take their holidays in places which are much further afield. Holidays in the United States of America are increasingly popular, and here the public power supply comes at different voltage and frequency (110 volts 60Hz) as compared with the European standard of 220/240 volts 50Hz. Even so, this does not pose a problem if your charger is switchable to the US standard, and it is a point you should check out first if you intend to use a European-standard camcorder in the United States.

Another point to bear in mind when you are taking a camcorder away with you on holiday is that you may wish to do check replays of your recordings on a colour set as you go along. You might take a colour portable with you, either an ordinary set or one of the new mini-screen LCD colour televisions. If on the other hand you have access to a colour television set at the place where you are staying, you may be able to use this instead, provided that it can be plugged into your camcorder's signal output and assuming that it is designed for use on the same television standard as the camcorder, eg UK PAL for machines sold in Great Britain (see page 187).

More on equipment

The remaining items of your video holiday baggage are all optional, but a plain glass filter to protect your lens from the elements is worth taking along. Alternatively, a UV filter to reduce distant haze, or a 'skylight' filter to cut the blue cast reflected from clear skies can be substituted to improve picture quality as well as protect the lens. If your camcorder has an earpiece socket, you should certainly slip one of these tiny accessories in your case. If you prefer to do a more thorough job of sound-monitoring, a better alternative to the earpiece is a pair of full-size headphones. Choose phones which have generously sized earmuffs as they will keep out the direct sound and allow you to concentrate on the audio signal itself. It is important to check that the earphones are correctly matched to the monitor-signal output; if you are uncertain on how to set about this, consult your dealer. Another audio item which need take up little room is an extension microphone, if you have the requisite camcorder socket. This is useful if only as means of eliminating the pick-up of camcorder operating noise in quiet conditions, should this happen to be a weakness of your machine. Finally, you may decide to take a tripod or one of the handier mini-tripods – plus a bag to carry your video gear around on shoots. The rigid cases which are supplied with some camcorders are bulky to have with you all the time, and a lighter padded bag with pockets to take small items will probably be more convenient. You are also likelier to be able to carry it through with you at airport check-ins.

Having reached your holiday destination, what are you going to record onto the tape? Is the emphasis going to be on people, places, or a bit of both? It's good idea to be clear on this at the outset; it's also a good idea to resist the temptation to start shooting whatever catches your eye the moment you arrive. So, unless there is some once only event going on – such as little green men arriving from outer space – restrain your enthusiasm and take a look round first, especially if the location is completely new to you.

Another factor which can have quite a major bearing on your approach is whether your video is to be edited in camera, that is recorded in the final shot order, or post-production edited into a different shot order on a copy tape. Post-production editing is a boon if you are uncertain as to what you will want to include in the final version of the video. You can shoot the material in any order, the edited movie can be built up from the best parts of the recording, and the overall shape of the movie can be finally determined when the material to be retained is known. If this is to be your approach see pages 108-118 for the actual process of post-production editing.

Narrative Structure

Whichever way you decide to produce your holiday movie you still need some kind of broad action-plan in your mind; without this, you will inevitably find that you have filled the tape with a lot of unrelated odds and ends. Remember: think in sequences (see

Chapter 5). Although this comes more naturally if the shots are primarily of human activity, it is equally true if the emphasis is on places rather than people.

To take an imaginary example: suppose you are wandering round the old town of a Mediterranean resort. Your first shot might well be a general view to show the character of the area, the town square and its traffic for instance. Now move in a little closer, and your next shot might show just one corner of the square which we can now see includes an attractive little feature: an ancient water-trough into which a cascade of water is pouring from the mouth of a gargoyle-like creature in stone. A still closer view shows us the detail of the cascade, and the passing traffic can be seen as a shivery reflection in the water of the trough. The next shot is of the traffic itself, and we pan with a quaint three-wheel vehicle as it passes by on its way to market with a cargo of onions.

Onions are the link to take us to the nearby open market where we see these and other vegetables on display. There is lively movement and chatter here, and the next few shots are quick cuts to show the activity at the various stalls. Now comes a cut to a deliberate contrast: the west front of the church, an impressive building which stands a little apart on the far side of the square. It is quieter here, and we hold the shot for a time to allow it to make its impact ...

This sequence is typical of what can be done in such surroundings once you have got your eye in and have begun to link your shots together visually or by association of ideas. It is certainly more fun to shoot video this way than to take unrelated pot-shots, and it is infinitely more interesting to watch.

Now let's imagine a sequence which is mostly about people, say a family who are spending a day on a sandy beach. Once again, the best way to open the sequence is to establish the location with a wide shot which shows the character of the setting: maybe it is one of those idyllic places which the crowds have not yet discovered, or perhaps it is crammed with people and overlooked by tourist hotels. Either way, the audience likes to know. Follow this with one or two closer shots which show the family against this background: the adults might be sunning themselves while the younger members of the family amuse themselves in more active ways – paddling, or playing beach football. Gradually, each successive shot brings us closer to the action and eventually to the actions of individuals, allowing us to see their expressions and hear whatever it is they are saying to each other. Finally, we are so close that we can see only the details of the actions: feet kicking beach balls, spades scooping up sand and so on.

This introduction to a scene and the gradual unfolding of the action within it may seem to be a rather academic restriction on the freedom of the cameraman, but it is a most important movie-making technique in the exploration of the location. Having achieved this, the camera can then pull back to a wider view and re-establish the general scene before closing in again to continue a probe of the setting and its activities.

Cuts, zooms and pans

This move in, pull back shooting pattern can become repetitious of course, and an effective variant is to begin with a sudden close-up of some piece of action, say the kicking of a ball, and then to move back to reveal the background to the action. To accomplish this, you can go from close-up to a wider view in any one of three ways:

1. Cut, move to a new position further away and at a different angle.
2. Cut, stay where you are but reframe the shot by zooming out to a wider angle before continuing the recording.
3. Keep running while zooming out.

Method 1 is the professional way and gives the most satisfying result on the screen. However, it takes time and effort and the action shown in the close-up may have changed or stopped by the time the wide shot begins, so there may be action matching problems. Method 2 is practical if the close-up was shot at a zoom setting which leaves sufficient range for the pull back, although cutting without a change of angle can give the appearance of a jump cut. Method 3 is, strictly speaking, only legitimate if the aim is to feature the gradual revealing of the background to the action;

otherwise, it is a slow and obtrusive alternative to a straight cut, and becomes tedious to watch if done to excess. Nonetheless, it does get over the problem of matching actions over the cut which can occur with methods 1 and 2.

Just as zooming should be done only for a good reason, panning is also a camera move which should be used sparingly if it is not to become visually irritating. One legitimate reason for panning is to follow the action; shots of beach football, for example, will need to pan to keep up with the play. The other legitimate reason for panning is to relate one part of the scene to another, a situation which can arise as a natural part of the action in this day on the beach sequence.

The safety of young children is a constant preoccupation of parents at the seaside. No sooner has a toddler begun to make for the water's edge than heads turn and adults prepare to go to the rescue. A situation like this can be covered very succinctly by panning from a shot of the mother to a view of the child who is receding into the distance. Quick thinking on the part of the father will soon have him sprinting after the runaway, and similarly quick thinking on the part of the camera operator will result in a cut from the distant child to one of the rescuer as he sets off. What not to do is to pan from the toddler back to the father, instead of cutting from one to the other. Hosepiping the camera back and forth is a bad technique: it makes the audience feel giddy and will soon have it heading for the way out.

Another reasonable but less dramatic use for a pan might be brought in earlier among the establishing shots if the aim is to show the relationship of a feature – an icecream stall, say – to the position of the family group. Begin this pan with a few seconds of static shot (remembering to allow for the backspace time) and continue the shot for a few more seconds when you reach the end of the pan.

Continuity and cutaways

To return now to the mother-and-child-on-beach situation, this relationship, and that between other individuals in the group, can be a fruitful source of additional story-continuity ideas. Viewers, when presented with a shot in which the subject is seen looking at something off the screen, will assume that the next shot will show whatever it was that the person was looking at. It does not matter whether this was really the case or not, the apparent connection between the two shots will be accepted unless there are compelling reasons which suggest the contrary – an abrupt and illogical change of location for instance.

Therefore, if a shot of the mother looking anxiously out of frame is immediately followed by one of her offspring, the two will connect in the minds of the viewers and another link in the story chain will have been formed. It becomes possible to envisage a sequence of shots in which real pieces of connected action are linked together by shots which are included to fill in the continuity gaps.

Hence, a sequence of shots might be: mother and toddler together on sands, toddler crawls out of picture leaving mother watching to see where it goes *cut*; an older child digging a sand castle cut; closer shot of mother looking out of picture in opposite direction, turns to look back in direction of *off-frame* toddler, *cut* from her to toddler who is now well on the way to the sea *cut*; father getting to his feet to go after child, pan with him as he sets off and catches up with the wanderer, they start to walk back to mother *cut*; the older child carries on with its castle-digging (see pages ii-v).

Note that although the actions of the mother, father and child might well have been part of one connected incident, the cuts to the first shot of the older child and to the shot of the father getting to his feet open up the possibility that the actions could in fact have been parts of separate but similar incidents which took place over a very much longer span of time; the shot of the father could well have been contrived specially, with the help of a little direction from the cameraman in between shots.

The shots of the older child are termed cutaways, and they serve the very useful purpose of bridging time-gaps and of hiding jumps in the action, for instance the jump between the mother looking in one direction at the end of one shot and looking in another at the beginning of the next. Cutaways are a great help when you are trying to build a sequence of events over which you have a little or no control. So whenever you are shooting action sequences like this one, shoot some extra scenes in case you have to make use of them as a means of smoothing the flow of the pictures as well as providing additional visual interest.

Having seen how it is possible to tell a story within a particular sequence, let's take a step back to consider how this might be made to relate to the story of a whole day on the sands. It begins with the arrival at the beach, the spreading of towels and the erection of wind-shields and so on after which the beach activities begin including the incident covered by the 'runaway toddler' sequence. Later, there is a picnic followed by more beach games, perhaps while the adults snooze in the sun. Finally, there is the departure from the sands at the end of the day.

While it is not necessary to cover all of these activities in detail it is important, if the interest of the audience is to be held, to show some indications of the passage of time. So shots of the family's arrival help to start things off, while the picnic marks the middle of the day and serves to break up what might otherwise be a too lengthy sequence of beach games.

Structure helps the viewers relate to what is going on; without it, they are lost in what amounts to a succession of unrelated snap-shots. Even the most tenuous thread of story is infinitely better than none at all. Moving back another step to a still wider canvas, the holiday as a whole should have an overall structure: preparations for the journey and the journey itself; arrival at the holiday destination; introductory shots of the immediate vicinity; a day on the beach; a visit to a place of interest; night-life, and so on ...

Thus, our holiday video turns out to be a series of boxes within boxes, of shots related to each other within sequences, and sequences related to each other within an overall structure which has to be made clear to the audience. If the emphasis is on people whose holiday activities are more or less self-explanatory, a main title (which can be pre-recorded onto the beginning of the tape or superimposed live over the opening shot by your camcorder's titling facility) may be all that is required to set the scene. For instance: 'Our Holiday in Wales' could say it all.

Commentary and subtitles

A holiday video which is basically a travelogue will probably need the help of sub-titles, or a commentary which can either be ad-libbed live at each showing or added to the sound track later. Commentary dubbing is a subject in itself (see page 136). An alternative to post-production commentary addition is to record explanatory comments in the form of speeches straight to camera as you go along. Talking right into the eye of the camcorder lens is either fun or something of an ordeal depending on the kind of person you are. It is easier to bring off if you have an assistant to hold the camcorder, otherwise, you have to set it up on a tripod or some other suitable support and switch it on with a remote control or time-delay. It is also better if you use an extension microphone rather than rely on the inbuilt one to pick up your words of wisdom.

If you intend to insert subtitles at a later editing stage (rather than superimposing them live at the time of shooting), you will need to reserve space for these on the tape by shooting overlength material which can subsequently be erased and over-recorded by the insert. If you don't, you may find yourself unable to add the subtitles because to do so would entail the loss of too many good shots.

The recording of fades to mark the beginning and end of a sequence is another of those chores which is easier to carry out during post-production editing than during live shooting. However, if you are editing in camera, and if your camcorder has a fade-button, it is quite practical to put the fades in as you go if you are organised enough to be able to pick the points at which they should come.

Camcorder Protection

Shooting video in unfamiliar surroundings raises potential hazards. On the coast, blowing sand and seaspray present obvious dangers to your camcorder's lens and interior mechanisms. It is sensible to keep the camcorder well protected in its carrying case when it is not being used and to keep it there when conditions are hostile. Remove the lens cap only when shooting, and fit a plain glass or UV filter over the lens to provide a first line of defence for its delicate surface. To further reduce the risk of internal damage from blown dust and grit, load the cassette into the camcorder in dust-free conditions indoors or in the car. If you are holidaying in a hot climate, do not expose the camcorder to the sun for long periods, and take a neutral density filter along with you if the light is likely to be particularly brilliant (sunlight on snow, for example) to avoid the risk of spoiling shots through over exposure.

CAUTION

Holiday environments can be tough on your camcorder, take the following precautions:

!   Keep the camcorder in its case when not in use.
! .   Remove the lens cap only when shooting.
!   Fit a plain glass, UV or skylight filter to protect the lens.
!   Load the cassette into the camcorder in dust-free conditions.
!   Do not expose the camcorder to the sun for long

Making better movies – the language of film

S o much for the nuts and bolts of shooting video; but what makes a movie work on screen?

Movies are a medium of communication, and over the years they have developed their own language of expression. It is a language which has to be learned, and this applies just as much to audiences as it does to movie makers. As a medium it is supreme among the arts in its ability to portray the real world, but it is in itself quite artificial, and it speaks to us by way of a pictorial language which first took shape during the early days of the silent cinema.

The major breakthrough came with the realisation that a story can be told in series of separate shots taken at different distances and from different angles. (Until this point, films had been shot in continuous takes by cameras which were fixed in position and set well back from the action.) This newer cinematic approach summarises the essential difference between the cinema and the theatre, and in order to make good video one must re-learn this important truth.

Hopefully, the technique of cutting from shot to shot in a controlled and purposeful way is already becoming second nature to you, as is the use of shoots of different sizes as a means of directing the attention of the viewer to where you wish it to go. Until now, though, we have glossed over descriptions of shot sizes, and the time has come to make these clearer.

The 'filmic' way to shoot a scene is to record it as a series of separate shots taken at different distances and angles. Here, two camera positions are being used alternatively to record a group of friends enjoying a drink in the sun. One camera position is for wide-angle views of the whole scene, while the nearer position in the foreground covers the details of the action.

wide-angle shots

close-shots

In all professional work for the cinema and television, shots are given standardised descriptions so that the camera operator knows exactly what is required. We may as well use these same descriptions even if there is no intention of shooting movies from detailed scripts, because they act as a useful discipline when we are shooting any kind of material.

These are standard shot descriptions:

Long Shot (LS)

A long shot is one which takes in the whole of a scene. It is some-times referred to as a wide shot, and one of its most important uses is to establish the nature of a location in the minds of the viewers. The actual distance between the camera and subject varies considerably depending on the circumstances. If, for example, the shot is of an expanse of countryside, the camera may be many hundreds of yards away from the main feature, say a group of trees. When the term is used in relation to the human figure, the camera distance then comes down from hundreds of yards to tens of feet. According to the standard description, a long shot of a human figure is one in which the figure takes up half to two thirds of the height of the picture. At longer ranges, for example where the subject is reduced to a silhouette on the horizon, the shot then becomes an Extreme Long Shot (ELS).

It helps if you know and use the correct names for each of the different shot sizes. The illustration shows all the main ones as related to the human figure: Extreme Long Shot (ELS), Long Shot (LS), Medium Long Shot (MLS), Medium Shot (MS), Medium Close-up (MCU), Close-up (CU), and Big Close-up (BCU). If the camera lens is zoomed during the action, a shot which begins as a Medium Long Shot can end as a Close-up – or vice-versa.

Medium Shot (MS)

In relation to the human figure, in medium shot the picture height includes a standing subject from (typically) just below the waist to the top of head. The figure is close enough to be easily identified and the expressions can clearly be seen, while enough of the background remains visible to place the subject in the setting. This is a frequently used shot as it covers the action without giving particular emphasis to any one part of it. Scenes containing dialogue are frequently shot at this camera range and where two characters are seen together the shot is described as a two-shot.

Shots taken at intermediate ranges between long shots and medium shots are called Medium Long Shots (MLS)

Close-up (CU)

Close-ups range from those which include the whole of the head and shoulders of a human subject to those in which only a part of the head is shown in 'big close-up' (BCU). Close-ups are frequently used to show the reactions of people to each other, and for 'talking heads'. Another use is to give dramatic emphasis to significant objects, for instance the muzzle of a gun. Shots which come midway between close-ups and medium shots are called Medium Close-ups (MCU).

In Chapter 6, we saw how to build a sequence set on a beach, beginning with establishing shots after which we grew gradually closer to the characters and their reactions to each other. In shot-size terms, the progression was 'LS to MLS, to MS, to CU'. Having first explored the scene in this way, the actions and reactions of the various individuals were shown in an interplay of shots ranging from medium close-ups to long shots, with a couple of close-ups included as cutaways. If you were to script this sequence, these are the size descriptions that you would write down against each of the shots.

Scripting

For scripting movies, there is a standard format in which each line represents a single shot. Unless there are instructions to the

On this typical page of shooting script are given the essential directions needed to set up for each shot in a sequence. It begins with a fade-in to an exterior scene – the Camp – which is to be shot in daylight. The first shot 'establishes' the scene in the minds of the audience, and it is followed by shots which are taken progressively closer to the action as the scene unfolds on the screen. The sound recording consists of the background noises natural to the location.

			Page 3
28	FADE IN		
	EXTERIOR		
	– THE CAMP, DAY		
	LS of the tent lines, plenty of activity going on		sync background sound
29	CUT to MLS of Camp kitchen; a meal is being prepared		Ditto
30	CUT to CU of steaming cauldron of soup		Ditto

contrary, the transition from shot to shot is by way of a straight cut. If you had been making the movie on film, the term cut would have been taken literally because each piece of cine film is physically cut and spliced onto the next. For video, the term is used metaphorically, but the effect on the screen is just the same.

In film language, the alternatives to a straight cut are fades in and out from one shot to the next, or dissolves (mixes). Both of these techniques are much slower transitions than cuts, and they are used to suggest the passage of time or the change from one location to another. Fades are well within the video repertoire of the average home video maker, and they can be done either on the camcorder while the shots are being taken or later at the editing stage when they are being copied during assembly. For adding fades, you will need to connect a video processor or enhancer into the editing set-up. Dissolves can also be edited in but require the use of rather more sophisticated equipment than for simple fades, that is a production mixer, because of the need to synchronise the picture feeds from two video machines. Production mixers with digital effects are also able to add wipes and other types of transition form shot to shot.

Cuts and Zooms on Action

Cuts on action are those which carry an action over from one shot to the next, and they constitute an important element in film making. However, they require the cuts to be made to high standards of accuracy so that the transition is made smoothly This presents problems when video is being edited unless frame-accurate editing equipment is being used – see Chapter 8. The fact that the video sound is cut with the pictures and not independently as a separate recording also creates problems, especially when intercutting shots containing dialogue. For these reasons, and because it is so easy to change the screen size of a shot by zooming in or out without stopping for a cut, the zoom (and the pan) are often used by amateurs instead of a straight cut.

For instance, the cinematic way to shoot a conversation between two people is to cut from one speaker to the other as the talk passes to and fro. The easier alternative for video is to record the scene as a two-shot (page 88), the static nature of which can be relieved by discreetly zooming in and panning between the two speakers from time to time and then zooming back to the two-shot. While it may be frowned on by purists, it is a practical way round the problem of cutting on dialogue, and if it is done with sensitivity it is not too obtrusive.

More on Continuity

Cutaways are a means of bridging jump-cuts, that is interruptions or discontinuities in the action, by briefly cutting to some related subject before returning to the main subject. They are, in fact, examples of the way that film can cover simultaneous but separate activities through the intercutting of parallel action. In early movies, the unsophisticated audiences of those days had to be helped over sudden changes from one scene to another with subtitles, for example: 'meanwhile, back at the ranch'. Nowadays, we are well used to this switching back and forth, and cutaways are used not only to hide jump-cuts but also to telescope time by making it possible to remove uninteresting parts of lengthy actions. Cut-ins, in which a close-up detail of something within the main shot is used, are similar to cutaways and serve much the same purpose, as well as providing dramatic emphasis.

Shot Length

Part of the art of film making is to know how long to allow for the length of each shot. Obviously, the content of a shot has a bearing

ms   cu (from
different angle)
cut on action

The cameraman is recording a 'cut on action' which is centred on the little girl's hand as it reaches down to pat the goat. Ideally, the cut from medium shot to close-up would come during the downward movement of the hand, but this degree of editing precision is often difficult for video. An easier edit is to let the hand reach the goat's back and to cut to close-up for the patting, a shot which should be taken from a different angle to the medium shot.

Parallel action cutting is a good way to increase the pace and interest of your movies. Here, a family group has just arrived at the giraffe's enclosure on a day out at the zoo (1). Meanwhile, two stragglers and a dog are running to catch up with the main party (2). As the giraffes begin to greet their visitors (3), the latecomers arrive to join in the fun (4). This intercutting of separate actions tells the story more vividly, and it allows the editor to 'telescope time' by shortening the length of the shots at the cuts.

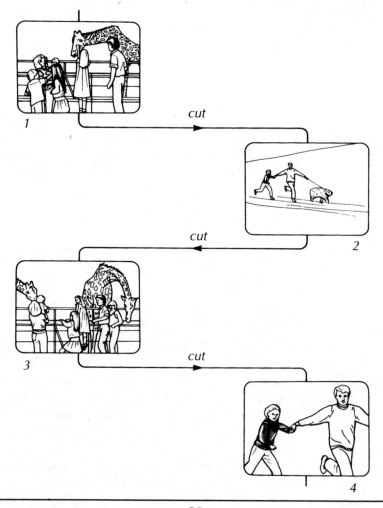

on its length; ideally, it should end just at the moment when the viewer has absorbed all the information in the scene, and is beginning to wonder what happens next. If you succeed in this, your cuts will be effectively invisible, and the images will flow smoothly.

In general, long shots run for longer than close-ups because they contain more information for the eye to take in, and an average length might be ten seconds or so. The detail in a close-up can often be assimilated in a flash, and most need only be held for two or three seconds unless the subject happens to be a 'talking head', in which case the sound, rather than the picture, governs the editing. Medium shots come between these two extremes, and the length of their stay is generally decided by the action; the shot is held for as long as something interesting is going on or being said.

The pace at which a sequence is cut also depends on the mood which it is intended to communicate. Slow cutting has an effect which is calming and relaxing, whereas faster cutting gives a feeling of drama and excitement. Controlling the mood in this way is not an easy thing to do while you are shooting live and editing in camera, there are too many other calls on your attention. It is, however, something to keep in the back of your mind on a shoot, and if you intend to carry out a post-production edit, pace can be a major factor in determining how you organise the assembly of your shots.

The 180° Rule

The actions of human characters involve a whole grammar of visual signals which the audience will pick up if it is given the right clues. For instance, there is the question of continuity of movement. If we see a character walking along a path to cross the screen say from right to left, and if this shot is immediately followed by one in which the same person is walking along the path from left to right, the viewer's natural assumption is that the walker has reversed direction and is now returning to his or her starting point.

In reality this may not be the case: the explanation could simply be that the camera position for the second shot has been shifted over to the other side of the path. Confusions of this kind can be avoided by keeping the camera anywhere within a 180-degree arc of the original position, hence the name '180 degree rule'. In other words, in the example given above, stay on the same side of the path for both shots! If for any reason you have to change sides, you can neutralize the effect of the apparent reversal of direction of movement by interposing a shot of the subject approaching (or receding) straight towards (or away from) the camera.

The same rule works for eyelines. Suppose you have a scene in which two characters are holding a conversation, and you are covering it in separate close-ups which cut from one to the other: these shots should both be taken from camera positions which are on the same side of an imaginary line connecting the two characters together. If you switch sides, the characters, judging by their eyelines, will no longer appear to be looking at each other.

Pictorial Composition

The pictorial composition of your shots is one of those areas where rules have grown up which, though seemingly arbitrary, actually work well in practice. For instance, the placing of the human figure within the frame has its conventions. Do not allow the joints in the figure to be cut by the edges of the frame, that is at the subject's ankles, knees, waist or neck. Choose instead a framing which cuts the figure, say, just above the knees or just below the shoulders.

The placing of the head in a close-up is important. If the subject is looking directly at the camera, the head should generally be placed centrally in the frame. Otherwise, if the subject is looking at something or someone out of the frame, the head should be set slightly off-centre so that there is a little more space to the edge of the frame in the direction in which the subject is looking; this is called looking room. You also need to allow headroom by leaving a little space between the top edge of the frame

To maintain the continuity of movement on the screen from shot to shot, the girl's walk along the path should be recorded from camera positions which are all within the '180 degree zone' on the same side of the path, eg at A and B. If shot 2 is taken from C, the audience becomes confused as the girl appears to have reversed her direction compared with shot 1. However, shot 2 can be taken from the 'wrong' side of the path if it is aimed from D directly on the line of the girl's approach; this frontal angle neutralises her previous left-to-right movement across the screen in the minds of the audience. The shot from D can be panned to follow her as she walks past (now from screen right to left), or it can be cut before the pan and continued as a separate shot from C.

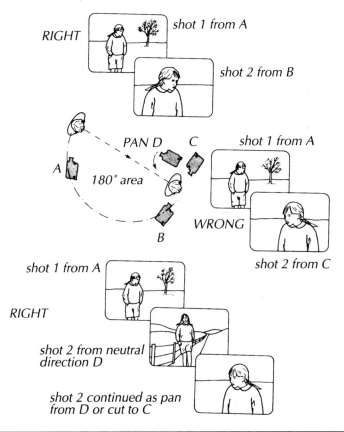

shot 1 from A

RIGHT

shot 2 from B

PAN D   C   shot 1 from A

A

180° area

WRONG

B   shot 2 from C

shot 1 from A

RIGHT

shot 2 from neutral direction D

shot 2 continued as pan from D or cut to C

and the subject's head, except for big close-ups when the rule is to set the head so that the eyes come at about two-thirds of the height of the picture. Walking room, as you might expect, is the allowance of extra space ahead of a moving subject which is being followed in a pan shot, whether a human figure, a vehicle or some other object.

There are also a few rules about pictorial balance. One is the 'thirds rule'. In this, the scene is divided into three sections both horizontally and vertically, and the idea is to line up the shot so that the main features are made to come at the intersections of the imaginary dividing lines. In practice, this is often difficult to achieve of course. However, a rule that is easier to remember and

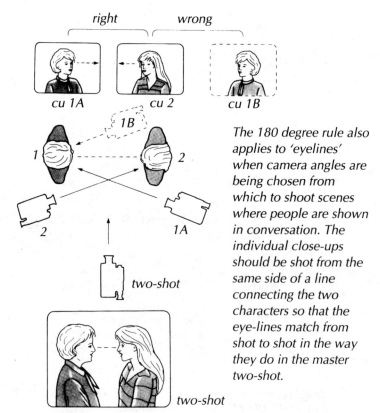

right   *wrong*

cu 1A   *cu 2*   *cu 1B*

1B

1   *2*

2   *1A*

two-shot

two-shot

The 180 degree rule also applies to 'eyelines' when camera angles are being chosen from which to shoot scenes where people are shown in conversation. The individual close-ups should be shot from the same side of a line connecting the two characters so that the eye-lines match from shot to shot in the way they do in the master two-shot.

to follow is: never allow the horizon in a scene to come exactly on the centre line of the frame. The reason for this is one of those questions of aesthetics, but it is true, nonetheless. Another fault to avoid is to shoot horizons which are not horizontal; it pays to line up your scenes carefully in the viewfinder.

Because the pictures are two-dimensional, it is all too easy to confuse the eye with an unsuitable choice of background. Beware of classic howlers such as trees growing out of tops of heads (the fact that the tree may be many yards to the rear of the head in question will not be apparent if there are no visual clues as to the depth of the scene). Depth is easier to convey pictorially if you avoid shooting your scenes square-on and go instead for diagonal compositions which lead the eye into the picture and direct it towards the centre of attention. The viewer's eye is also kept happier if the centre of attention is in the same position within the frame before and after each cut.

Irrespective of the composition, any movement within the frame will become the centre of attention. Where movement is a major element in a scene, such as in a shot of a passing vehicle, a diagonal composition is generally the most effective and pleasing to watch because of the increased illusion of depth. Also, as compared with a shot in which the subject traverses the picture directly from one side to the other, the diagonal movement gives the eye longer in which to take in what is going on and it reduces the need to pan the camera to follow the subject.

High and Low Angle

The vertical angle at which a shot is taken is another important visual signal. Scenes which are viewed at normal eye level convey the message that this is a normal situation: dramatically, it is neutral. On the other hand, a shot taken from a high angle to look down on the subject diminishes it and evokes a feeling of superiority in the viewer. Conversely, shots taken from a low angle impart a feeling of inferiority or weakness. High and low angles are often used as point-of-view shots in which we are seeing the scenes through the eyes of one of the characters.

There are right and wrong ways of framing the human figure.
(1) This is incorrect: the lower edge of the frame cuts the body inelegantly at the elbow joint.

(2) Both of these two framings are acceptable: the body is cut either just below or just above the elbow joint.

(3) Wrong: the body is cut at the knees – which often looks awkward.

(4) Right: Framing to cut the body just below or just above the kneejoint is much better.

(1) The big close-up has been carefully composed. The top of the head is cut by the top edge of the frame while the chin is just clear of the lower edge. The girl is looking off-screen to the right, so she has been placed to the left of the frame to give her 'looking room'.

(2) The character in this close-up is speaking direct to camera, so she has been placed centrally in frame. The head is less than full frame height and a space has been left at the top of the picture to give her 'head room'.

(3) A lively subject for a medium long shot. As the camera pans left with this tennis player it is aimed slightly ahead of him to balance the shot by allowing 'walking room'.

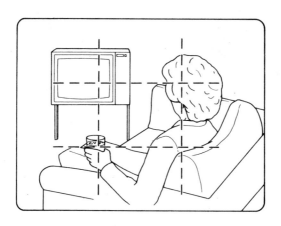

Some pictorial compositions have a natural balance which is based on the 'rule of thirds'. In this shot the TV screen, the glass, the woman's head and shoulder – the main points of interest in the scene – all coincide with the intersections of imaginary lines which divide the frame into equal thirds. While it is not always possible in practice to achieve this degree of balance, it is an ideal to keep in mind when shots containing a number of different visual elements are being set up.

Since film is a language which is expressed primarily in visual terms, it makes sense to plan your movies in a visual way, and the technique of storyboarding is often used for this reason. A storyboard is a script presented as a series of drawings, so that the composition of each shot, and the flow of images from shot to shot, can be designed into a movie from the earliest stages. The pictures can also be a great help to the camera team when the movie is being recorded.

Sound

Although the visuals are the most important part of film-making, sound also has an important part to play, and music can be used as a powerful creator of mood and atmosphere. The selection of music to be added to a movie soundtrack is governed partly by common sense and partly by fashion – saccharin-sweet string accompaniments to romantic scenes are no longer popular in the commercial cinema, for example. In the amateur sphere, the choice of music for holiday travelogues often follows traditional lines, such as the selection of ländler music for video shot in the Austrian Tyrol. Music as a background for drama is a much trickier area, but you should err on the side of understatement. If you overdo the atmosphere, the effect is likely to be comic rather than dramatic.

Problems of taste can also arise on the selection of music backgrounds for scenes of domestic life because the mood to be reinforced is more personal and it is all too easy to lapse into embarrassing banality. The lightest of touches is required here: avoid heavily orchestrated music and opt instead for small ensembles or solo instruments – or leave out the music altogether and let the natural sound carry the scene.

When you are planning musical additions to your soundtracks, remember that the law of copyright protects all commercial music recordings except those which have been specially produced for use as background music. This applies to all soundtracks whether made for professional or non-profit amateur use unless the latter are limited to showing in the home. Copyright-cleared background music recordings can be obtained by mail order, and the addresses to contact are to be found in the relevant hobby magazines. From this source comes a good choice of discs and tapes offering mood music with titles describing the content in filmic terms such as 'busy street', 'quiet countryside', and so on.

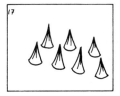

high-angle ls of tent-lines

closer view of lines. A scout with water bucket

cu – bucket placed under tap

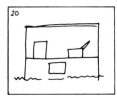

mls of field kitchen

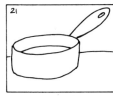

cu – pan of soup on stove

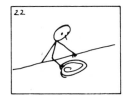

ms – one of the cooks at work

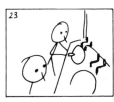

ms – at the wash-basins

cu of face reflected in the water – hands dip in and break up reflection

cu – a face being vigorously towelled dry

The technique of storyboarding can be a great help in the planning of a movie. No real artistic skill is required – just the ability to produce simple sketches which show the essentials of each shot in a sequence in terms of its content, screen size and camera angle. This is an efficient and easy way to work out your story ideas in advance by translating them into film language before shooting begins.

Shots taken from a low angle make subjects look forbidding, while a high angle has the opposite effect. Cut from one to the other and you create opportunities for humour or drama.

Moral: avoid placing your performers against unsuitable backgrounds!

Video and sound editing

Having by now produced one or two very presentable videos by the direct method of editing in camera, you may be ready to move on to carrying out some post-production editing as a way of overcoming the limitations of in-camera editing and further improving the standard of your work.

In its fullest form, post-production editing involves the complete re-arrangement of the shot material into a different and better order by assembling it onto a copy tape. The need for this editing by copying, which requires the use of a second video machine of course, is brought about because it is not possible to edit video tapes by physically cutting and rejoining them as you would a cine film. Video pictures are recorded in the form of over-lapping magnetic signals which cannot be cut and respliced without severely disrupting the pictures when the tape is played back. We shall be looking in detail at the full routine for carrying out an assemble edit later in this chapter. A limited amount of post-production editing can, however, be carried out on the original recording, either on the camcorder or on a second VCR depending on the facilities available. This direct editing involves the recording in of video inserts and/or audio dubs.

Video Inserts

Video inserts are very useful as an editing tool, though the scope for carrying them out on your camcorder is reduced if, as is probable, it does not have a video-in socket for the insertion of pre-recorded material. Inserts such as live action shot through the lens, or titles generated electronically within the camcorder or shot from a title card can be made, however. Shooting title cards, which have to be specially prepared, set up and lit, is a skilled activity in itself, and the techniques are explained fully on page 182.

If your VCR has Insert Edit, you can transfer the camcorder tape to this machine if it is of the same format, (eg VHS-C), and use it to carry out the edit instead. The basic routine is the same as for camcorder-edited inserts but with the advantage that, since the VCR will have a video-in socket, pre-recorded live action can be edited-in from off another tape (eg fed from off the camcorder) provided that the new material is of a length suitable to fit into the length of tape which is being over-recorded. Bear in mind that this insert will be a second generation copy of the camera original. The set-up is simply one of connecting the video-out of the camcorder to the video-in of the VCR, and the routine is, in fact, similar to the one used for assemble editing – a topic we shall come to shortly – but without the audio connections needing to be used.

To record any kind of insert, you first have to decide where it is to come within the existing recording, that is the material which is to be over-recorded and therefore lost. Hopefully, you will have anticipated this by having shot some spare length which can be sacrificed to make room for the insert, the edit in and edit out points for which are located on the tape with the help of the cue/review buttons.

The insert procedure itself varies somewhat from model to model, but the essence of it is to arrange for the over-recording to end at a pre-determined out point. This bit of juggling is introduced into the process partly because you may be working blind. If you are using your camcorder to play back the insert materials onto the VCR, its viewfinder will be displaying, not a playback of the shot which is being displaced, but the material which is displacing it. To help you end the insert at the correct place therefore, you first zero the VCR's tape counter at the out-point and then run the tape back to the in-point, after which you switch

Step-by-Step to Video Inserts (Titles)

1   Prepare, set up and light a suitable title card.

2   Decide where insert is to fall within existing recording.

3   Zero the tape counter at the out-point.

4   Run the tape back to the in-point.

5   Switch to insert mode and press camera start button. (The title insertion ends as the counter reaches zero.)

to insert mode and press both play buttons. On most machines, the insert recording ends automatically as the counter reaches zero again.

Inserts, in the generally accepted sense of the word, change only the pictures, the original sound continuing over it unaffected. 8mm, with its inability to dub audio separately, inserts both new pictures and sound together. True inserts are a useful means of cutting away from the main subject to some subsidiary action while keeping the original sound going under the insert. Apart from their ability to give extra liveliness to a sequence, they can also be used to hide any awkward jump cuts in the action!

Audio Dub

Audio dub replaces the original mono sound with new material. There are several reasons why you may wish to do this. One is to add commentary or music. Another is to substitute a background effect where a shot is spoiled by unsatisfactory location sound, perhaps due to wind noise. In such cases, the shots can often be saved by dubbing in suitable backgrounds of a kind which does not need to be closely synchronised to the pictures.

Audio dubbing is a simple set-up by which original video sound can be dubbed out and replaced by new sound such as background effects or music. For this, the 'line' output of a sound-source such as a cassette recorder is connected to the audio input of a video recorder (or camcorder) having the audio dub facility. The dub is monitored on a TV set as shown, and the sound level can be adjusted manually by means of a volume control connected into the lead between the two machines; alternatively, one channel of an audio mixer can be used as a volume controller.

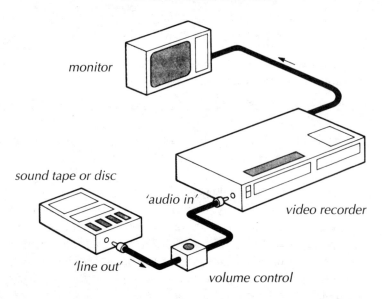

Another reason for dubbing new audio is that you may wish to edit out jump-cuts in the sound at some of the picture-edits. For example, if music was being played in the background at the time the shots were being taken, the breaks in the music at each shot change will be very noticeable and the remedy may then be to replace the original sound with a continuous background.

Nowadays, a wide choice of effects recordings is available for amateur use. Alternatively, you can record your own effects on cassette (see Chapter 10).

Step-by-Step to Audio Dubbing

1   Connect a length of screened cable from the sound-source machine's audio-out socket to the audio-in socket on the camcorder or VCR. (If 'mic' socket, use attenuator lead.)

2   To control the level of dub manually, use a simple volume control connected into the line or use one channel of an audio mixer as a volume controller.

3   Check that chosen sound effect is long enough.

4   Find the point at which the dub should start on the video tape. Hold machine on play-pause and switch to dub.

5   Pre-test the sound effect level, release the machines together and run the dub to the end.

To make an audio dub, the sound is transferred from the source recording by means of a cable connection. You will need a screened cable about one metre in length and with the correct plug terminations; these can be bought ready made-up at hi-fi stores. The connections are made between the source machine's line-out (or audio-out) socket and the audio-in socket on the VCR or camcorder, whichever is recording the dub. If the latter socket is marked 'mic' instead, you will need to make the connection via an attenuation lead which reduces the level of the signal to match the microphone-level input.

Although this set-up can work well as it stands, a useful refinement is to add a means by which the level of the dub can be controlled manually. For the electronically minded, one method is to obtain a 25 Kohm volume control from a radio spares shop, mount this in a metal box to screen it from hum pick-up and connect it into the audio dub line. An easier alternative is to use one channel of an audio mixer as a volume controller.

To make the dub, begin by checking that the chosen effect is of sufficient length. Then, having found the point on the video tape where the dub is to commence, hold the machine on play-pause and switch to dub mode. Pre-test the effect level, release the machines together and run the dub to the end, being careful not to overrun into the next section of the video tape. On VHS machines with both hi-fi and mono sound, the dubbed mono and original

When multi-track sound mixing is being carried out it is necessary to cue the various tracks in and out to a precisely laid-down programme, a task which is made much easier by reference to a 'dope sheet'. This example page, which is set out at one second of runtime per line, shows that the original sync sound transfers continue without a break, but additional background sound (voices) is to be faded in at the beginning of shot 18. It also shows that the next section of commentary is cued to commence half way through shot 17 and that there is no musical background at this point in the movie.

Page 4		Sync Fx	Bkgnd Fx	Music	V/O
17	MS: Signal changes to green 1-25				
18	ELS: Up the line—steam plume 1-31				
			Voices		

hi-fi tracks can be heard together, or, on some advanced machines, mixed together onto the mono track.

Video Copying

Although putting inserts and dubs onto original video tapes is quite straightforward, it does carry the risk that, if you make a mistake, you may ruin an irreplaceable recording. For this reason, many people prefer to keep their camera originals as shot and carry out all their editing operations on a copy.

There are other grounds for wishing to make copies of original video recordings:

1. You may want to change the format, say from 8mm to VHS, so that it can be played back on your table-top VCR.

2. You may wish to add commentary and/or music to the original synchronised sound, an operation which is not possible by means of simple audio dub, which erases the original sound.

3. You may wish to carry out a full post-production assemble edit.

Step-by-Step to Copying

1   Obtain two video machines, one of which can be the camcorder.

2   Use screened cable running between video-out and video-in sockets to make machine-to-machine video connection.

3   Make audio connections as for an audio dub (see pages 98-99).

4   Connect television set to record-machine.

5   To make a copy, start both machines together from off play-pause and record-pause respectively and run to end of recording.

This is a two-machine set-up by which original video recordings can be transferred onto copy tapes. In this case, the transfer is being made off a camcorder which is acting as the source-machine; the record-machine is a VCR which need not be of the same format. Additional sound, ie commentary, music or effects, can be mixed to the original sound recording during the transfer, which is done non-stop. As well as simple copying, assemble editing can be carried out on a stop-start basis under manual control of the machines provided that the VCR has the backspace edit facility. A single TV screen can be used to monitor playback off each machine in turn, or a 'picture-in-picture' set-up can be used instead.

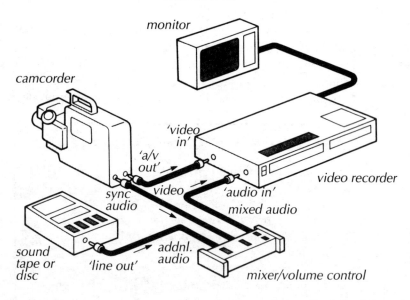

Let us look at each of these options in turn. Video recordings can be copied quite easily provided that you have the use of two machines, one of which can be your camcorder while the other would be a video recorder. In the basic set-up, the machine-to-machine video connection is made by screened cable. This is run between the respective video-out and video-in sockets, the plug terminations being either scart, phono, BNC or a combination of these. The audio connections are made in a similar way to that used for an audio dub, except that the source-machine is now a camcorder (or a VCR). As before, a simple volume control or one channel of a mixer may be used to control the sound level as it is being transferred.

An ordinary TV set is all that is required to monitor both pictures and sound. It is connected to the record machine but it can be used to display the pictures from *both* machines in turn: when the record-machine is in either record or stop mode, playback from the source-machine is displayed; when the record-machine is in playback mode, however, it has priority for the screen and its own pictures are displayed.

To make a transfer, you simply start both machines together from off play-pause and record-pause respectively and run to the end of the recording. The resulting copy, being at one remove from the original, is thus a second generation tape, and it will be slightly lower in quality than the original. The quality loss, however, is minimised if you use premium-grade tapes such as Extra High Grade or PRO. If you are recording on a Super-format such as S-VHS, though, the copying loss will be barely discernible, and you could go on to make a copy-of-a-copy (ie third generation) without noticeable fall-off. Third generation copies of standard-format originals are generally of so poor a quality as to be unacceptable. This is why video makers who wish to run third generation copies off second generation edited masters use hi-band tapes for all their work.

If your source and re-record machines each have an edit switch, use of this will help to optimise the video signal for transfer and reduce the copying losses. A more radical improvement can be obtained by the use of a video enhancer. These are electronic devices which are connected into the video transfer line, and they not only optimise the signal for copying but enable you to control the picture brightness and colour; fades can be added as well. Some of the more expensive enhancers, or processors, can produce trick effects (see Chapter 14), and practically all of them incorporate audio mixing facilities.

Adding Music

Suppose now that you wish to add music to a video recording while the transfer of both pictures and original sound is being made onto a copy tape. This is an operation which can be carried out without the need for a separate audio dub facility on the record machine.

To do this, you connect a music source such as a cassette player, to the second channel of the audio mixer, the combined output from which is fed to the record machine as before. The transfer is made non-stop, during which the levels of synchronised sound and music are adjusted individually to mix them in and out as required.

Non-stop mix-transfers are a three-handed job, and you will need the help of an assistant to cue-in the music material and to take care of the changing of source cassettes on the replay machine if required. A better and more organised way of handling the music feed, though, is to pre-record it onto a cued sound tape which can then be fed to the mixer non-stop.

There are a number of ways of cueing a sound tape, but the simplest way is to record a guide onto a spare track to show where each section of the music should start and end. To record this guide-track, you set the tape to a start-mark and the tape recorder to record-pause; the video tape is set on play-pause on the first frame of picture. You then release both machines together, calling out the music cues into a microphone connected to the tape recorder while you watch the pictures on the screen. Having recorded the guide-track, you then convert the sound cues to tape-counter references, or mark their positions on the back of the tape with a wax pencil or felt-tip pen. Preferably, the sound recorder will be a reel-to-reel machine with 1/4inch tape as this is much easier to work with, but a cassette machine is quite a practical alternative.

When you are pre-recording the music, remember to record it at a constant high level so that you can make all the level adjustments downwards when the final transfer is made onto the video

Using Natural Light

The bright sky area in the shot above makes the automatic exposure system reduce the lens aperture and under-expose the figures in the foreground.

The giraffes on the right were first seen positioned against the sky. To avoid backlight exposure problems, they have been re-angled to appear against a darker background.

Over-contrast: *flesh tones can often burn out in bright sunlight. Shoot against light backgrounds to lower the exposure and reduce the risk of over-exposure on highlights.*

Auto-focus: *check that your auto-focus is focusing on the tiger and not on the bars of his cage; if in doubt, focus manually.*

Making a Holiday Movie

This establishing shot sets the scene for the viewers and shows the family arriving for their day on the beach.

The camera has come in closer for this next shot. We can see their expressions, and how they relate to each other as a group.

A close-up of the boy; this can be used as a cutaway to hide any awkward jump-cuts.

Mother and baby sister find things to occupy them.

If you are good at speaking to camera, this is one way of keeping the viewers informed.

Loading or unloading? This shot could be used either to begin the movie or to end it.

Three-lamp Lighting Set-up

The basic lighting set-up incorporates three lamps. The first to be set is the backlight. This provides a rim of light to separate the subject from the background.

The key light is then added, angled on to subject from alongside the camera. It provides the main source of illumination and modelling.

The diffused fill light is now placed on the other side of the camera. Its function is to reduce the harshness of the modelling and to lighten the shadow areas.

Sound Recording

Recording good sound is a job in itself, so take an assistant along on those important shoots.

An extension microphone can be taken right up to the source of the wanted sound and kept well away from camcorder operating noise.

Video Interviews

This set-up gives three-quarter profiles of the interviewee in close-up and includes the interviewer over-the-shoulder at wide-angle.

If the interviewee is seen talking to the (off-shot) interviewer, place his head slightly off-centre to give him 'looking room'.

Step-by-Step to Adding Music While Copying Video

1   Connect a music source (e.g. cassette) to the second channel of the audio mixer and dub direct, or

2   Pre-record a music tape to timed lengths for dubbing.
(a)   Cue the sound tape by recording a guide-track to indicate where each section of the music should start and end: set the tape to a start-mark; set tape recorder to record-pause; set the video tape to play-pause on the first frame of picture; release both machines together calling out music cues into a microphone connected to the tape recorder while you watch the pictures on screen.
(b)   Connect music source to the sound tape recorder. Use the guide-track to cue sections of music into place on the sound tape.

3   Dub the music onto the video tape:
(a)   Set up as for video copying, with the audio line carrying the original sound connected via one channel of an audio mixer.
(b)   Connect the music replay machine to another channel of the mixer; set on start-cue to play-pause.
(c)   Reset the video machines to start-cues on play-pause/record-pause respectively; release all machines and run the copy transfer while mixing the original sound and pre-recorded music.

tape; this minimises tape hiss. Where there are to be music fades in and out at the transfer, leave plenty of overlap at the beginnings and endings of the pre-recorded sections to give yourself ample working margins at the mixing stage.

If the video is to end with music, you should arrange for the last note to come at the end of the last shot. To do this, use a stopwatch to time the length of music required, and the actual length of the music on the source recording. The amount by which the latter is over-length is the length of time that you should allow the source recording to run before you begin the transfer onto the cued tape; the music will then end exactly on cue.

A word of warning here: although video recorders have tape drives which are speed-controlled to high standards of accuracy, sound recorders tend to drift in speed. The running time for a twenty-minute sound tape, for instance, might vary by several seconds either way at each playing depending on the quality of the machine. Hence, the extent to which you will be able to match the timings of the video and sound tapes during transfers will depend on the performance of your particular sound recorder.

Adding Commentary

While the exact timings of music transfers may not be too critical, the addition of voice-over commentary usually calls for greater precision. One method, which by-passes the problems of tape-to-tape synchronisation, is to speak it direct to a microphone which records it straight onto the video tape via the mixer during a non-stop transfer. However, speaking commentary while watching the screen for cues is not easy, and if you make a mistake you have to go right back to the beginning and start all over again.

A method which you may prefer is to pre-record your commentary section-by-section onto a sound tape; this tape is not cued, and the sections follow each other with gaps of only a second or so between them. The video transfer is done non-stop as before, and each section of voice-over is added during the transfer by stopping and starting the commentary tape in step with the pictures. This neatly side-steps the problem of sound tape speed drift, but it does require the help of an assistant to handle the machines and manage the mixer level controls.

This method of commentary addition works quite satisfactorily provided that there is no music to be mixed in as well. If there is, and if both music and commentary are to be pre-recorded onto parallel tracks of a cued tape, the stop-start transfer routine cannot

The editing bench becomes more crowded as the basic set-up is expanded to include an edit controller, which is used to operate both video machines automatically, and an enhancer to improve the picture quality of the transfer. The arrangement also includes for the dubbing of pre-mixed sound from a reel-to-reel recorder, the signals from which are fed to the audio mixer section of the enhancer via a graphic equaliser in order to optimise the audio quality. Having been processed on the enhancer, both video and audio signals are then passed to the recording VCR.

Fades can be added to pictures and sound as the edit proceeds, and some units are able to change the character of the pictures in various ways as described in Chapter 14. The ultimate in sophistication is achieved by the incorporation of video mixing (which requires the use of an additional source VCR which must be gen-locked to the other source VCR), and video-sync control of the sound recorder, which permits the lift-off and lay-back of the original sound to allow it to be mixed with additional sound without loss of synchronisation.

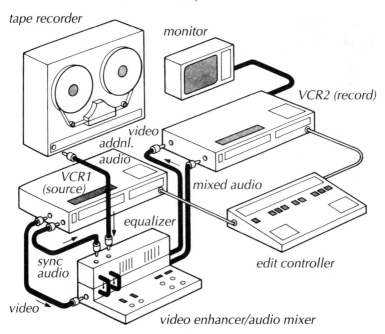

tape recorder

monitor

VCR2 (record)

video
addnl.
audio

VCR1
(source)

mixed audio

equalizer

edit controller

sync
audio

video

video enhancer/audio mixer

be used: the sound tape has to be run non-stop and we are then back with problems of tape-to-tape synchronisation.

One way round the problem is to script your commentary so that it does not depend on being recorded to accurate timings. The 'professional' way, though, is to do the transfer on a special sound recorder which is synchronised electronically to the actual video pictures. These machines are rather expensive, but they make it possible to lift off the original sync sound from the video tape, combine it with additional sound (held either on separate tracks or pre-mixed on the recorder via 'sound on sound' mixing), and then to lay it back onto the video tape still in perfect synchronisation. If you have access to an additional VCR, a cheaper way of ensuring that your commentary does not get out of sync with the pictures is to make a mute temporary copy (ie pictures only, no sound) of the original video on a separate video tape and to audio dub your commentary, section by section, onto this copy tape. It can then be fed as an audio source to a third channel of the mixer during the video transfer and mixed onto the final video tape.

Full Post-production Editing

We come now to a full post-production assemble edit in which the camera-original material is completely re-arranged as it is copied onto a second tape. Although this involves the use of rather advanced techniques compared with the running of simple transfers and dubs, many enthusiasts believe that this type of editing is essential to the making of 'real' movies, and look on it as the key creative element in their video activities. It is certainly true that assemble editing has a major effect on the scope of the subjects that can be covered, and also on how they are recorded.

Because the material can be shot in any order, there are none of the limitations of edit-in-camera recording. The intercutting of parallel actions – which can be shot at different times and in different places – can all be done at the editing stage, and you are free to try your hand at risky shots safe in the knowledge that any failure can be edited out later. The beginnings and the endings of shots can be trimmed down to exact lengths and, given sufficient editing skills and technical resource, even cuts on action can be included in your movies. At the other end of the scale, the most rambling and unplanned holiday and family videos can be edited into quite watchable movies provided that they contain material which can be re-ordered into some semblance of continuity.

The set-up for assemble editing is similar to the one used for making copy transfers but with the important qualification that assembly is a stop-start process. Although automatic edit controllers can be included in the set-up to simplify and speed up the process, the basic essentials are the same whether the job is done automatically or manually. The routine will therefore be described in manual terms before we consider the advantages of investing in a controller.

Assembly consists of the location and transfer, a shot at a time, of the camera-original material onto a copy tape in the required revised order. An edit is therefore made at the start of each shot, and this means that the record machine should be capable of making clean edits, in other words, that it should have the back-space facility (see page 41). If your table-top VCR has this, together with still-frame and frame advance, it can be used as an editing recorder. Both feed and record machines should have cue/revue picture search to speed up the location and setting of edit points, this being the most time-consuming part of the process.

One of the difficulties of editing video manually is to allow for the 'backspace' or 'pre-roll' time on the VCR which is doing the re-recording. This is the time which the machine takes after being released from record-pause to lock onto the control track at the end of the previous recording and so make a clean edit as it begins to record the next segment. Because of this, if the feed and record machines are released off pause simultaneously to begin the assembly of the next shot onto the copy tape, the beginning of the new material will be lost while the record machine completes its backspacing routine. There is no standard backspace time for video machines generally, but it is commonly of one to two seconds duration. For some edits, this loss will not be of great significance and can be ignored. However, there are times when it can be of vital importance and needs to be taken into account. It is possible to make approximate allowance for backspace by releasing the source-machine off play-pause about one second late. A better and more accurate method is to set the edit-in point on the source-tape early by the amount of the backspace, so that the true edit-in point reaches the playback head just as the record-machine completes the backspace and starts to record.

In this case, the setting of the edit-point on the source-tape can be done by a stopwatch. First, you time the length of the material to be trimmed at the beginning of the shot, and subtract from it the amount of the backspace; this shorter length is then the point at which you set the tape early for the edit-in. With this in mind, when you are shooting camera-originals which are to be assemble – edited later, shoot them with at least five seconds of spare length at the beginning of each shot; this not only facilitates the offsetting of the backspace but also helps to ensure that the edits will be stable on the copy.

The backspace time can be measured exactly by test-copying a shot and comparing its length with that of the original – the difference between the two is the backspace. The measurement can be done with maximum accuracy by counting frames if you have frame-advance. Or, you can increase the accuracy of stop-watch timings by running the playbacks in slow-motion and correcting them to the normal-speed equivalents. As a final refine-ment, you will probably find that the last few frames of each shot on the copy assembly are over-recorded at the edits. This over-recording can also be measured and offset by running the edit-point on the record-machine forward by the corresponding number of frames.

These routines may all seem to be rather complicated and fiddly, but they are simpler to follow than their descriptions might suggest. If you are using one or more 'editing decks', that is VCRs which have features which are specially provided for facilitating the editing of video, you will be able to assemble your tapes quickly and accurately. These machines, which are comparatively new to the domestic market, have jog shuttle dials with the aid of which you can rapidly pinpoint edits by playing the tapes back and forth at any speed you like from single-frame and slo-mo to five or more times faster than normal. They are also capable of making high quality picture transfers because of their advanced circuitry and mechanical design, and if your feed VCR has the facility to play the picture in reverse a frame at a time, the setting-back of the feed tape to a point which is ahead of the true edit-point can be done quite easily. All this having been said, however, the use of an edit controller in which the backspace edit offset can be pre-programmed will obviously speed things up and reduce the work-load in lots of other ways.

Edit Controller Systems

Edit controllers work by remotely operating the tape transports and other facilities of the feed and record machines on which your edit system may be based. This being so, it is vitally important to realise that the machines must be compatible with the controller and its operating system. To appreciate this more fully, we first need to take a look at the various types of system on offer, beginning with the simplest.

Synchro edit is a method whereby a camcorder acting as the feed or source deck is linked via a 'synchro-lead' to a VCR as record deck. No external edit controller is used, the synchro-lead being all that is required to make the camcorder operate the VCR's remote record-pause function. To make this system work with anything like reasonable frame-accuracy, both machines need to have matching pre-roll facilities to offset the backspace time correctly and therefore generally have to be of the same make.

Duet edit is somewhat similar, but works simply by releasing both machines off pause simultaneously without reference to back-space pre-roll and hence the edit-in will not be accurately timed.

Automatic edit controller: this is a microprocessor-controlled device which both operates the feed and record machines automatically and holds the edit-point details of a given number of cuts in its memory. It then instructs the feed machine to replay these in the correct order for assembly onto the copy tape. The machines must therefore be fitted with means to communicate with the controller, either via infra-red control sensors as is common on VCRs, or by a control terminal port as is usual on camcorders. The controller therefore needs to 'know' the infra-red control code for the particular VCR and the camcorder remote control system linked to its edit terminal. The two most common camcorder edit control systems are Control-L (or LANC) for 8mm, and RMC (or Panasonic 5-pin), a system to be found on some VHS/VHS-C machines. Edit controllers are available either as dedicated devices designed to work only with particular makes and types of camcorders and VCRs or as universal types which are intended to operate a wide variety of video machines.

A new development called time-coding is in the process of revolutionising video editing at the advanced amateur level. Under this type of system, each frame of video picture is 'labelled' with its own reference number relating to the number of hours, minutes, seconds and frames which have elapsed since the beginning of the recording. There are two rival systems, namely VITC (Vertical Interval Time Code), and RCTC (Rewritable Consumer Time Code).

They operate in basically the same way, but VITC coding has to be recorded onto the tape (of course without being visible in the picture), at the time of shooting or while being copied onto a second tape; RCTC coding on the other hand can be carried out at any stage of the editing process, and so is the more flexible of the two systems.

Each type of coding is used with compatible edit control equipment, and frame accuracy is virtually 100 per cent when edits are made with these time-code systems.

Whatever the system, to carry out an automatic edit you first need to establish the edit details in much the same way as for manual editing. You then key them into the controller's memory, whereupon the controller takes over and does the job automatically. Some controllers have a titling feature, and others include an audio mixer in their facilities. However, it is true to say that a full audio edit with added music and commentary will often need to be done as a separate operation after the particular segment of the video assembly has been completed. Other than this, the whole process of finding, previewing and recording edits is greatly simplified and speeded up, and with the advanced systems, if more than one edited copy tape is required, the extra copies can be easily assembled from off the original recordings and not as third generation copies off an edited master – with obvious advantages in terms of picture quality.

There are two other key devices which can be brought into play when videos are being edited. The first is a video processor, a facility which is a development of the simple enhancer mentioned earlier in this chapter. Processors are devices which apply digital manipulation of the video signal not only to enhance it but also to change it by the addition of various effects. Simple enhancement involves the variation of the picture brightness (including fades to and from black), its contrast or its colour intensity; some can correct the colour balance by varying the levels of the red, green and blue components of the picture individually. The sharpness of the picture can be increased or decreased, a facility which can be useful to reduce picture shimmer on some types of subject such as patterns in clothing.

Full processors take things a stage further by adding such effects as wipes and mixes, techniques which involve the synchronising of the video signals from different sources by means of devices called 'genlocks'. Other effects which can be added to the edited copy are 'mosaic', which turns the image into coloured blocks, 'poster' which gives a cartoonlike effect, and 'strobe' which gives a jerky appearance to the action.

'Picture-in-picture' (PIP) is yet another way of combining images from different video sources and showing them separately on the one screen. Many processors have 'split-screen', a facility which can be used to display the 'before and after' effect of any processing which is being done.

For the ultimate in editing technology, you can computerise your editing operations. Computer software packages are now coming onto the market which can be used with personal computers (PCs) to enable them to control editing operations. While some operate in much the same way as microprocessor-based edit controllers – except that many have unlimited edit memory storage – others are beginning to extend their capabilities into much wider areas. Digital storage of edit decisions, interfaces for generating and scrolling titles, Chromakey, vision mixing and other editing tools are beginning to appear, albeit at professional levels of cost and computer memory.

Whatever you decide, if you are considering the purchase of an automatic controller as a part of your editing set-up, check first that it is compatible with both your video machines, by test if possible, before you commit to buying. And, before we get carried away by this dazzling technology, it is as well to recognise that all this automation will not produce good videos if the operator of the equipment is lacking in the knowledge of editing principles and in creative ability!

Video Editing – the Nuts and Bolts

To get down to the nuts and bolts of video editing then, the material should first be logged in the form of a shot-list giving brief descriptions of the shots, their tape counter references and preferably their running times. A good method of compiling the list is to record a running commentary onto a cassette tape while you watch a replay of the material; this is then converted into a written list. The cumulative timings for the start of each shot are then taken by stopwatch and entered on the list, from which the individual shot lengths can be worked out.

If the originals are being shot to a numbered shooting script, it makes the material easier to identify for editing if you record the shot number onto the beginning of each take. The professionals use clapper-boards for this, but sheets of paper with the numbers written in felt-tip pen can be held up to the camera, and they serve just as well.

Having made your preparations, the routine for assembling each shot is as follows:

Step-by-Step to Full Post-Production Assemble Edit Manual Control

1 Two video machines, one of which (the record machine) must have backspace (or fine edit), are set uo as for video copying.

2 With the record-machine on stop, locate the shot to be assembled on the source machine; hold it on play-pause at the point where its assembly onto the copy tape is to begin, ie the edit-in point.

3 Locate the point on the copy tape where the assembly of this shot is to begin, and hold the machine on record-pause.

4 Release both machines off pause simultaneously and run to beyond the end of the shot. Go to stop on both machines. (Note: if your equipment has synchro-edit, you will be able to release the machines from off the one button.)

5 Check the edit on the copy and then repeat the above routine to the end of the assembly.

6 For greater editing accuracy, set the tape on the source machine early by the amount of the backspace time, ie about one second.

On amateur equipment, the process of shot assembly is a strictly sequential one: each shot has to be copied and edited to length one by one in the correct order. If you reach the end of an assembly and then wish to change your mind about one of the edits, you will have to repeat, not only that edit, but all the others from that point onwards. It therefore pays to check as you go! The only exceptions to the sequential rule are inserts, which can be added in without affecting any of the other material provided that they are of the same length as the material which they are replacing. The video set-up for inserts is the same as for assemble editing.

Before you start on an assembly, you will find it helpful to write down an editing decision list. This could be in the form of

This is a page from a plan compiled to help the editor to assemble shots in the correct order. The shot numbers are given along the left-hand side of the sheet together with a brief description of each shot. In the centre are the tape counter hours, minutes and seconds ('real time') references to assist in the location of the material on the source tape, to the right of which are reminders as to how each edit is to be made. Note from the counter readings that shot 17 was obviously recorded as an extra after the material for the arrival of the train had been taken.

			Page 2
16	LS of station platform: a few passengers are waiting for the train	0672	Delete 1st 6 secs run for 9 secs
17	MS: the signal changes to green	0851	Cut in 2 secs before signal changes, run for 6 secs.
18	ELS: up the line - a plume of steam (whistle)	0695	run for 8 secs

simple notes, but a better way is to compile a revised-order shot list in which the details are given together with other editing information (eg 'delete first six seconds') to help you set up the edit-points quickly.

How you decide on the assembly order is very much a matter of personal judgement, but the principles of shot to shot continuity, the function of cutaways, and the ordering of your material into a logical progression of images which tell a story, all follow the same rules as for in-camera editing. Now, though, you have the flexibility of being able to try different shot orders, and to repeat the edits until you are satisfied that the best use has been made of the material available. In fact, you can experiment with cuts and juxtapositions *ad infinitum,* because the originals are unaffected and can be recopied as many times as you like.

One important editing chore is to 'top and tail' shots to give tidy beginnings and endings, especially if subjects are entering or leaving the shot. Entrances should be preceded by only a few frames of 'dead' action, and exits should be equally neat.

Assembling the Material

This juggling with material is quite a fascinating task. Suppose, for instance, you have shot some video on a harbour-front. Down below, some fishermen are working on their boat to prepare for sea. The editing problem is that this particular group of shots ends with the boat's abrupt departure – we go suddenly from shots of the men at work to one in which the boat is already in motion; in effect, we have a jump-cut, and your task as editor if to find some way of bridging the gap in the action.

Suppose also that, on another day, you had taken some shots of the unloading of a catch at the same location. Among these are several medium close-shots of the crowd of onlookers and the angle is such that the boat itself is not visible on shot.

The answer to the problem of the jump-cut, then, is to 'lift' one or more of the onlooker close-ups out of context for cutting into the preparation sequence just before the shot of the moving boat. The jump between static boat and moving boat is then hidden. When you are on a location shoot, in fact, it is always a good idea to take a few extra shots for possible use as cutaways to get you out of difficulties. In this example, it is probable that the background sound to the cutaway will match the rest of the sequence. If it doesn't, you will have to dub in new matching background sound. This could either be taken from an effects record, or you could transfer some real location sound from off the original video recording.

If it is your intention to add a fully scripted commentary, you will need to work out the timings. The easiest format for the script is one in which the shot details are written down on one side of the page, while the corresponding words of commentary are written opposite them on the other side. Use lined paper for this, and reckon each line as one second of running time. You can then write the commentary at the rate of three words per line, this being the average speed at which voice-overs are spoken.

The style of your commentary should reflect the style of your movie. A simple family record should be equally simple in its choice of words and spoken in a natural and relaxed tone of voice. A holiday travelogue set in some exotic location might on the other hand merit a slightly more expansive style to suit the circumstances. Leave plenty of breathing space between the sections of speech so that your audience is not bombarded with too much information at a time, and don't allow the commentary to describe things which can already be seen on the screen; instead, use it to complement the pictures and provide additional (but relevant) information. For instance, the words 'inshore fishing isn't an easy life' might add something which cannot be gathered from pictures alone.

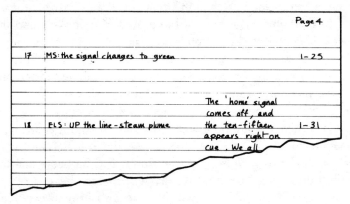

A convenient layout for scripting commentary: the page is divided into two columns, the shot details being on the left and the commentary wording on the right. Each line of script represents one second of running time and the words are written down at the normal speaking rate of three per second. The cumulative runtimes from the beginning of the movie are given at the right hand edge of the page in minutes and seconds. This format makes it easy to fit the words to the (edited) pictures and to cue them to the start of each section so that they all come at the right place when they are being recorded onto the video sound track.

Better lighting 9

Today's camcorders are amazingly good at producing pictures in quite dim lighting. Most can operate at illumination levels down to 10 lux or less – the equivalent of candle-light – and it is a fact that video can be shot in almost any conditions short of the proverbial coal cellar at midnight. However, there is no denying that the picture quality does suffer at these low levels; the colours become increasingly weak and washed-out looking, and the sharpness of the definition falls off because the lens is having to work at its maximum aperture. The camcorder's electronics are also working flat-out, and this gives the picture a somewhat coarse and grainy appearance.

Using Available Light

Sometimes you will not mind this too much: the freedom to shoot in whatever light happens to be available can outweigh these shortcomings. There will be occasions, though, when you will need to produce the best-looking pictures that you possibly can – perhaps of an important family event. It then makes sense to make the effort to improve the lighting. This does not necessarily mean you have to go the extent of bringing in high-power floodlights together with their attendant supply-cables. This would certainly increase the level of the lighting but it would also tend to change the character of the setting, and the presence of floodlights works against any wish to keep the atmosphere of an occasion informal.

The first move, therefore, is to see whether the level of the available lighting can be improved without making any radical changes. For instance, if the video is to be shot in a domestic setting such as a lounge where the top lighting is provided by a three-or-four-lamp pendant fitting, you may be able to substitute lamps of higher wattage for the ones which are normally fitted.

However, you should take care not to risk overloading the electrical wiring in the process, and you should certainly not attempt to use photoflood bulbs in ordinary domestic fittings as they not only draw a lot of current but they also run very hot and could possibly cause a fire.

Although this adaptation may have succeeded in improving the general light level, you can do more by adding to the illumination of individual areas, so take a look at what other light sources are available. Can the table and standard lamps be used to better advantage by moving them to different positions? Can the power of the bulbs be increased? Often they can, by sensible amounts, depending on the size and style of the shades and fittings. Are there any domestic spotlamps around? If so, they can be used to boost the lighting by aiming it where it is most needed.

Bounce Lighting

Nine times out of ten, careful attention to the redeployment of existing sources of illumination will improve matters sufficiently to enable you to shoot good pictures. If this strategy fails, however, you then have to resort to sterner measures in the shape of video floodlights. Although few performers really enjoy working under the glare of high-power lights, their use is sometimes essential, and the most acceptable way to use them for the illumination of small areas is to employ the technique known as bounce-lighting.

As the name suggests, this consists of bouncing the light off reflective surfaces instead of aiming it directly at the subject. If the walls and ceiling of the room are white or near-white in colour, the lamps can be turned upwards over the heads of the performers who are then illuminated indirectly by the reflected light. Alternatively, the light can be bounced off special reflectors, and sheets of white expanded polystyrene are ideal for this purpose.

Bounce light is diffused and soft in character, and hence similar to normal room lighting. The modelling of the subjects is very natural, and lighting-spread is such that performers can move about in reasonable freedom without running into areas which are over or underlit. The one drawback is that bounce is not very effi-

Bounce light is aimed upwards at the walls and ceiling for reflection back onto the subject below. These surfaces should be white in colour; if they are not suitable, some other reflective surfaces can be used instead.

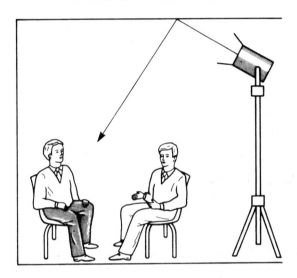

cient in its use of lighting power compared with direct lighting, and you may find that the illumination level is on the low side unless you are using floodlamps of high wattage.

Lighting Units

To meet this need, high-power video lights have been developed from earlier photographic types which are capable of being run for long periods at full power. Although photoflood bulbs in aluminium reflectors are still used, they have largely been supplanted by the newer and much more efficient halogen quartz lamps, and these are available in a variety of power ratings.

Portable video lights are of comparatively low power and range. Some are fitted to the accessory shoe on the top of camcorders and operate off their own battery supplies. Others are fitted as permanent onboard lighting units fed off the camcorder battery, and are arranged for either manual control or, in some cases, auto on/off as and when the ambient light level drops to a predetermined value. As they constitute a significant drain on the camcorder's battery, they do reduce the shooting time per charge.

There are also higher power (300 watt) mains-fed portable lamps which represent the upper limit in terms of heat output and weight for camera-mounted lamps. These units are very useful because of their portability, but single-lamp frontal lighting is not very flattering.

For more normal requirements, and where a greater spread of illumination and better photographic quality is called for, it becomes necessary to use bigger lighting units which have to be supported on tripod stands. There are quite a number of different types to choose from, and the lamp wattages range from 500 to 1000 watts, with a further doubling to 2000 watts for twin-lamp units.

In spite of the high efficiency of halogen lamps, the heat which they generate is considerable, and the 1000 and 2000 watt units are generally blower-cooled. This inevitably produces a certain amount of fan noise which may give problems with sound recording. Most, however, are reasonably quiet in operation and can be used in studio conditions provided that they are kept away from the microphones. For ultra-quiet lighting duties, uncooled 500/600 watt lamps can be used instead, and even the humble photoflood (275 or 500 watts) can be called into service.

Floodlights are available either as wide-beam units for general lighting, or in the form of spot-lamps the light from which is focused into a concentrated beam; some have variable-focus lamps and can be used for either duty. All have safety-glasses fitted which double as diffusers, and most incorporate sets of hinged flaps, called barn doors, which are used to direct the beam. The more expensive models have provision for mounting filters and extra diffusers to soften the beam further and correct the colour temperature of the light as required.

Halogen lamps give excellent service, but the bulbs are fairly expensive to replace. Their working lives (up to about fifteen hours) can be maximised if you handle them with care, so avoid subjecting them to mechanical shocks when in use; switch off and allow them to cool before moving them around on the set. Bulb-life is also related to the number of times that they are switched on and off. The heavy surge of current at switch-on is minimised if pairs of lamps are switched to operate in 'series' at reduced power while setting up is being done, after which they are switched to full power in 'parallel' for the take. Some units have series/parallel switching built in; otherwise this has to be provided by plugging pairs of units into an external series/parallel switch arrangement.

Three-lamp Set-up

For video shoots in which individuals or groups of people are to be lit by direct floodlighting, the exact placing of the lamps becomes more important. The basic lighting arrangement is known as the three-lamp set-up. The first of the three lamps is referred to as the backlight, and its function is to provide a rim of light from behind the subject in order to separate it from the back-ground. A spotlight is often used for this, as it concentrates the beam and allows it to be aimed very precisely at areas such as shoulders and tops of heads.

Having set the backlight, bring in the key light, so called because it provides the photographic modelling and sets the general level of exposure. Set it, not frontally, but at an angle onto the subject from a position alongside the camera, and aim it downwards at about forty-five degrees to the horizontal.

The light is quite strongly directional, and to avoid excessive variations in contrast within the depth of the scene you should set the light as far back from the subject as possible within limits of what is acceptable to give a good exposure, each doubling of the distance reducing the brightness of the scene by a factor of four.

The third lamp is now brought in. This is called the fill light, and it is set on the other side of the camera to reduce the depth of the shadows and to soften the modelling of the subject. It is gener-ally fitted with an additional diffuser such as a glass cloth scrim, and positioned so as to give a lighting intensity of about one half of that of the key light.

To this standard arrangement, a fourth lamp is frequently brought into play to light the background separately and to neutralise any double shadows cast by the key and fill lights. The illumination of the background should be set to a somewhat lower level than for the foreground to give depth to the scene and add prominence to the subject. You can, of course, extend this lighting set-up to cover larger areas at the cost of providing and running more lamps. If you are limited to a three-lamp set-up, your subjects have to remain within a fairly small area, otherwise the lighting becomes unbalanced and the performers may even stray into unlit areas.

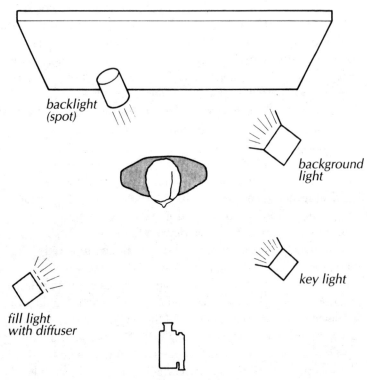

The complete three-lamp set-up as seen from above. An optional fourth light is often added, as shown, to illuminate the background.

Mixing of Artificial With Daylight

We have already touched on the question of mixed artificial and daylighting in an earlier chapter. A typical example is one in which the subject is sitting in a window lit by daylight. If the dark side of the subject is lit with artificial light, the difference in the colour of the two kinds of lighting is immediately apparent: the day side is cool in colour, perhaps even with a blueish tinge, while the artificial side is warm, probably with an exaggerated reddish cast. There is no white balance setting which will resolve this colour conflict, and an alternative lighting solution has to be found to give the colours their proper values.

The simplest method is to switch off the lights and to lighten the shadow areas by reflecting some of the daylight back onto the subject. Provided that the shot is a reasonably close one, and that the subject stays in the one position, this arrangement will give you excellent results with the minimum of cost and effort. All kinds of things can be used as reflectors: projection screens; aluminium foil which has been crumpled, roughly straightened out and stuck onto a sheet of hardboard; or purpose-made reflectors bought from photographic dealers.

An alternative solution to the mixed light problem is to change the colour of one light source to match the other. The easiest option is usually to 'cool down' the floodlighting by fitting correction filters over the lamps. You can purchase suitable blue filters at lamp or theatrical specialists, and the type known as half-blue is the best for general purposes. Some of the lighting power will be absorbed by the filter which will therefore get hot, and it should be made of a filter-gel which is sufficiently heat-resistant.

For lighting large areas, you may instead find it preferable to 'warm up' the daylight by taping sheets of orange filter material over the windows. This material is known as WF Orange, and it can be bought in large rolls. It is rather expensive, but it can be re-used.

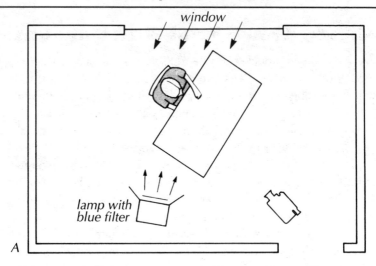

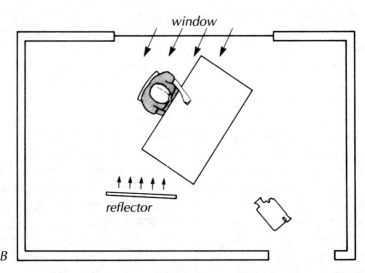

In set-up A, the subject is lit by daylight from the window. To lighten the shadow side, a floodlamp has been brought in to provide additional illumination. Note that a blue correction filter is being used on the lamp to match its 'colour' to that of the daylight. Set up B shows an alternative lighting arrangement in which the floodlamp has been replaced by a simple reflector.

Power Supplies

Large interiors such as church halls and workshops are difficult if not impossible to light to the standards which are the norm for small interiors. Many lighting units would be needed and, since large amounts of electrical power would be needed to run them, the distribution system of many buildings of this type would be overloaded.

Professional television crews, in fact, bring their own power generators with them to enable them to light large areas. Amateurs, perforce, have to settle for less expensive solutions, and the low minimum illumination levels at which domestic camcorders can operate often makes it possible to get by with just the available lighting supplemented with additional lighting to lift the foreground.

In the theatre, stage lighting varies in brightness, but is often sufficient for video recording purposes, even if only as an aid to rehearsals. If the performance can be staged specially for video, this opens up the possibility of bringing in extra lamps and interrupting the action at agreed points to shift the lighting round to suit the camera.

As already noted, video lights are great consumers of electric power: for every 1000 watts of light a current of just over 4 amps at 240 volts is required, so safe working practices are paramount when you are setting up and using high-power lamps. Use a separate mains socket for each lamp unit, and spread the electrical load over as many circuits as you can to keep within the current ratings. Use only power cables of the correct capacity for the duty, and run them as neatly and directly as circumstances permit. If cables are being stored on drums, wind them completely off the coil before connecting them to the load; otherwise they may overheat in use. Do not allow the cables or their connections to become wet.

To end on this note of safety, warn everyone on the set to beware of coming into contact with the hot surfaces of lamps, especially metal barn doors. Ensure also that the tripod stands are set up securely and that they are in no danger of being accidentally upset by the comings and goings of performers and camera crew.

10 Better Sound Recording

As we have already seen, built-in camcorder microphones have their limitations. They are prone to picking up camcorder machine and handling noise and are not very good at recording speech if the source is more than a metre or so away from the camera. In addition, there is no provision for manual control of the sound level on most models, and a further difficulty is that there are times when a single microphone is not sufficient to do the job properly in any case. Fortunately, all of these problems can be solved if your camcorder is fitted with a socket for an extension microphone.

Microphone Types

If you are unfamiliar with these, you may be uncertain as to how to select a suitable microphone from the many different kinds which are available, as a glance at the shelves of your local electronics store will show you. There are two reasons for this diversity: microphones have differing pick-up characteristics depending on their intended use; and they differ in the ways in which they convert sound into electrical signals. There are two basic types of pick-up pattern, namely omnidirectional and unidirectional.

Omnidirectional microphones are designed to pick up sound equally in all directions; the one on your camcorder may be omnidirectional. 'Omnis' are very good at capturing the general atmosphere of a location but, since they are not directionally selective, unwanted sound coming from sources outside the picture area may result in the shots being spoiled.

Unidirectional microphones have a pick-up pattern which is biased in the forward direction, a characteristic which is sometimes referred to as cardioid because of the heart-shape of the pattern. Microphones of this type pick up sound which is mainly from sources within the picture area, and the nuisance of unwanted noises-off is much reduced. It is quite possible that your camcorder's microphone is a 'uni' rather than an 'omni'. On the whole, unis are to be preferred for video work because of their ability to relate what you hear to what you see. Some extension microphones are super-directional; these are used in situations where their high selectivity is needed to record sound in difficult conditions.

Turning now to the ways in which microphones generate their signals, the cheapest types use a crystal, but their quality is poor and they are not recommended for video. Electret microphones use a polarised condenser instead of a crystal. The level and quality of their signal output is good, they are moderately priced, and they are very suitable for general use; however, they require a battery to operate them. Dynamic microphones work rather like miniature loudspeakers in reverse. The quality is excellent, and they do not require a battery. They are suitable for

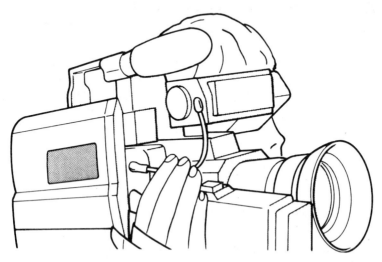

Camcorder microphones are liable to pick up operating noises as well as the wanted sounds!

general use and especially for music recording. Microphones are designed in various styles and sizes according to the particular application.

Stick microphones

These can be mounted on a stand or held in the hand, and are available in both electret and dynamic types and with both 'omni' and 'uni' pick-up patterns. Stick-mikes are the all-rounders of the audio world, but when used for video their size makes then clearly visible on shot. There are times when this is quite accept-able, such as for street interviews or music recording, but they are not suitable for drama unless they are mounted on a boom.

Tie-clip microphones

These are miniature electret mikes which are specially recom-mended for speech recording when the microphone should be visually unobtrusive. They are attached to the speaker's clothing and are virtually invisible on shot. Positioned within a few inches of the speaker's lips, they produce a strong speech signal which stands out clearly against noisy backgrounds. However, if there is more than one speaker, each has to be provided with an indi-vidual microphone, and the speech signals therefore have to be fed to the camcorder via an audio mixer; hence, tie-clip mikes are not suitable for use with large groups of people. Ordinary cable-connected tie-clips are quite inexpensive but they limit freedom of movement. As an alternative, radio versions are now available at economic prices; these allow virtually unrestricted movement to the wearer, the signals being picked up by a special receiver which passes them on to the camcorder via a short cable connection.

Gun microphone

These are super-directional microphones which are aimed at indi-vidual speakers or sound sources; they therefore require skilled operation by a sound assistant who monitors the signal on head-phones. Gun-mikes are generally restricted to outdoor use;

indoors, sound reflections off walls defeat the directional characteristics to a large extent.

Boom microphones

These are uni-directional microphones mounted on booms which can be swung overhead and aimed at individual speakers; they are often used for recording drama, and require skilled operation by an assistant. Although purpose-made units are expensive to buy, ordinary hand-microphones attached to simple booms make an acceptable alternative for amateur use.

Which Microphone?

	Mount	*Size*	*Suitability*
Stick	stand-held or hand-held	large, visible on shot	good for general use, street interviews or music recording
Tie-clip	attached to speaker's clothing	small and unobtrusive	good for speech recording – individuals not groups
Gun	operated by sound assistant	(off shot)	good in situations where it can be aimed at individual speakers or sound sources
Boom	on boom operated by sound assistant	(off shot)	good for recording speech, eg drama

Audio Mixers

As we have already noted, audio mixers are used to combine the signals from a number of microphones, and they can also be used as volume controllers. Simple mixers can in fact be made up cheaply by enthusiasts from published circuits, but these have largely been supplanted by modestly priced commercial units which incorporate battery or mains-fed circuitry capable of delivering better balanced outputs of higher quality. These are obtainable from hi-fi and electronics stores and also by mail order.

If you purchase an audio mixer, you might consider one which has built-in level meters. These are very useful, as they enable you to balance up the individual microphone inputs with a degree of precision which is not easy to achieve simply by listening on headphones. Remember too that you will be inputting the microphone signal to the camcorder 'mic' socket via the mixer. The mixer should therefore have a matching mic-level output; if not, it should be connected to the camcorder through an attenuation lead. At the beginning of a recording session, start by asking each speaker in turn to say a few words. The differences in voice levels will show up clearly on the meter, and you can then adjust the mixer settings accordingly.

When you are making these settings, go for levels which give good, solid recordings but are not so high as to overload the tape on signal peaks. If you do set too high, you may find that the first syllable spoken after a pause is distorted, especially on p's and b's, after which the overall level of the recording drops to a lower value as the speaker continues; during the next pause in speech, the background slowly returns to its original value until the speech resumes, whereupon it falls again. This cyclical fluctuation in volume is due to the operation of the camcorder's automatic gain control which is all the time trying to maintain a constant sound level irrespective of the natural level of the incoming signal, an effect which makes it impossible to reproduce true audio perspectives.

The problem can be solved neatly by setting the mixer output so that the signal peaks at levels which are just below the threshold at which the automatic gain control comes into operation. You can find this setting by trial and error by getting someone to speak steadily into the microphone while you gradually bring up the mixer level from zero to the point at which the volume, as monitored on headphones or VU meter, ceases to rise. This represents the threshold maximum within which you can work – from this point downwards you can control all your sound levels manually on the mixer, and background levels will not drift upwards during pauses.

Room Acoustics

Indoors, you may have trouble with the acoustics of the room in which you are recording. If the speech sounds 'boxy' or 'boomy', this will be due to sound reflections off walls and other surfaces. These can spoil an otherwise good recording, though the effect can be lessened by using close-position tie-clip microphones in place of hand or stand-mounted mikes. Any hard, flat surfaces will reflect sound to some degree, and this includes not only walls and ceilings but also uncurtained windows, table-tops and parquet floors. The solution is to muffle as many of these surfaces as you can: tables should be covered, floors should be carpeted, and windows should be curtained unless it is essential to admit daylight to the scene.

Tone Control

If, in spite of these precautions, your recordings still have an unpleasantly boomy quality, you will then need to apply some tone correction, either while you are making the original recording or at a later editing-transfer stage. For this you will need a tone correction unit of a kind which can be plugged into the appropriate points on the cable connections. Mixers with inbuilt tone controls are becoming available as a convenient alternative.

The most sophisticated and flexible type of tone control is the graphic equaliser (EQ), a facility which can be obtained either in the form of a free-standing unit or built into amplifiers. These apply very selective filtration of unwanted audio frequencies. With one of these you can, at editing for instance, remove just those parts of the signal which are responsible for boominess or tape hiss, leaving the remainder of the signal unchanged. It is also possible to tailor the sound in other ways such as adding extra bass for increased depth or treble for improved clarity.

EQ units generally have two channels so that they can be used for stereo, but the channels can be operated separately so that two mono signals can be corrected individually. If you use an equaliser during your video editing sessions, carefully check the effect of each adjustment as you go, by monitoring the sound over a loudspeaker (headphones may not give a true impression of how the tone corrections will sound when played back in normal way). Most EQ units have line level inputs which are not suitable for direct microphone connection, but low level microphone signals can be matched by feeding them via an amplification stage, a facility which is provided on most mixers.

For all your sound recording, take care to ensure that your microphone leads and audio connections are electrically sound and properly screened from hum pick-up, so that the signal arrives at the camcorder or edit deck in the best possible condition. Keep the length of extension leads as short as you can to reduce the risk of them picking up stray radiations from nearby electrical appliances and short wave broadcasts such as taxi radio messages. Do not operate microphones, mixers or other such equipment in close proximity to television sets and loudspeakers as these emit magnetic fields which can adversely affect the working of your audio systems.

Microphone Techniques

There are right and wrong ways of handling microphones for speech recording. Hand-held stick microphones – except the very expensive professional ones – are prone to pick up handling noise. It is important to get your performers to hold the mike in a firm grip and to keep it and its connecting cable as still as possible while recording is in progress. Another point for them to remember is not to speak directly at the microphone but to aim instead just over the top of it; this is to reduce the pick-up of

In this recording set-up, two tie-clip microphones are connected to a microphone mixer, the mic-level output from which is fed to the camcorder's external microphone socket via an optional tone control unit. The incoming signal is monitored at the camcorder on headphones. Provided that the mixer is a battery-operated type, the set-up is fully mobile and can be used for outdoor as well as indoor locations. For stereo hi-fi recording, the microphones are connected all the way to the camcorder via separate right and left hand mixer channels, the mixer being set to mono for 'centre-stage' speech recording, otherwise to stereo.

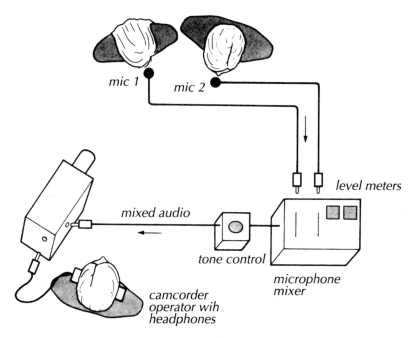

breath noises and the distortion of plosive consonants. Perhaps the most difficult skill for amateur performers to acquire, though, is the art of speaking to microphone at a constant voice level: most tend to start off strongly as they launch into their speeches, but gradually tail off as they reach the end. If you then lift the mixer level to compensate, the background noise comes up too, and this can be very noticeable.

Probably the most demanding kind of speech recording is that of voice-over commentary – it is so easy to make it sound embarrassingly amateurish. Commentary should be delivered at an even pace, without over-emphasis, and completely free of 'fluffs' such as mispronounced words, hesitations and other departures from perfection. If you make any kind of a mistake, you should re-record the offending passage there and then.

Any feelings of strain will inevitably show up in your voice, so you should try to make the recording set-up as comfortable and convenient as you can. If you use a stick-microphone, support it on a stand and position it as close as possible while allowing enough room for you to handle the script without rustling noises getting onto the recording. Some people prefer to hold the script; others like to read off a lectern, which can be simply a tray propped up on a couple of books. Position the microphone to suit your speaking height when reading from the script, and check that the operating noise of the video or sound recorder will not be picked up, by siting it out of microphone range. This will probably require the equipment to be controlled by an assistant, who can also take care of the timings and cueing of the sections.

Although you will have to speak a little more slowly and clearly than you do normally, you should nevertheless make it sound as natural as you can. If you have a regional accent, don't be tempted to try to disguise it, in all probability it will simply sound affected. However, do avoid the use of slang or dialect expressions unless the context calls directly for such deviations from normal speech.

If you can, memorise the script section by section, so that you only need refer to it occasionally for confirmation. Make a few test recordings before you start the session in earnest in order to get used to the set-up and to check that the wording sounds as good when spoken as it looks on the page. Play these tests back and listen to them critically. Is the pace and pitch of your voice suited to the material? Is the recording quality as good as it can be? When everything is ready, begin the recording, and never be satisfied with second best!

Check List

When speaking into the microphone:

* *Hold the microphone in a firm grip and keep it still.*
* *Aim over the top of the microphone rather than at it.*
* *Speak at a constant level.*
* *Re-record any 'fluffs'.*
* *Avoid any strain. Speak from a comfortable position.*
* *Speak a little more slowly and clearly than normal but keep it natural.*

Sound Effects

Taping your own 'wild', that is unsynchronised background sound effects is another interesting part of video movie making: it can become almost a hobby in itself. It needs little in the way of special equipment other than a portable cassette recorder and microphone, and many a pleasant hour can be spent in collecting background sounds of various kinds. It is, in fact, sensible to take your sound recorder along with you whenever you set off on a major shoot. It can then be used in spare moments to provide you with recordings of matching background sound, which can be dubbed in at editing if need be to replace any unsatisfactory sections of the original synchronised sound.

Record your background effects tapes at as high a level as possible to minimise tape hiss, and go for longish recording runs to give yourself plenty of margin at editing. Remember also to record effects of a kind which do not need to be closely synchronised to the pictures. For instance, if you are taping a traffic effect, keep back from the roadside so that the passing of individual vehicles merges into the general roar. Also, avoid backgrounds in which individual voices can be clearly heard: aim instead for a general babble.

Keep the content of each effect simple – do not allow it to contain too many different elements at once. If, say, you are recording a beach effect, it could include the sea, the cry of gulls, and even distant voices. But if there is a band playing within earshot, move on and find a better location!

As an alternative to carrying round a separate sound recorder, you could record background sound onto the camcorder tape simply by pointing the camera towards the source of the sound without regard to the picture recording. The audio off this section can be copied later onto a sound tape, after which this part of the camcorder tape can be re-used for a fresh recording.

Bear in mind that your video tapes may contain audio material which can be copied onto sound tapes to add to your effects library. Any material which runs for half a minute or so is worth considering, and you can stretch these times to any length by repeat-recording them nose-to-tail for as many times as needed to make up the required length. However, check that there are no sounds which are likely to be noticed each time they come round on the repeats.

As your stock of effects grows, you will need to catalogue them by tape-number and counter-reference so that you can find them easily when you need them. These lists could also be extended to include your collection of commercially produced effects, discs and tapes.

Stereo Sound

Stereo sound is featured on many video recorders and camcorders, and it seems that it is only a matter of time before it becomes standard as for sound recorders. This is already bringing in its train a whole new generation of stereo-related audio products including microphones – together with a whole new set of audio problems for you to solve!

One consideration is the question of 'stereo spread'. If your camcorder is fitted with a good quality stereo microphone, you will find that it will be capable of producing a stereo signal which has plenty of 'depth' for the recording of the ambient background sound at locations. Problems do arise, however, when speech is being recorded. As we have already seen, if speech is to be recorded clearly it is best picked up by an extension microphone positioned close to the speaker. If there is more than one speaker, a separate microphone should be provided for each.

If dialogue is being taped in stereo, the signals from the individual speakers should not be given a pronounced left and right stereo bias if this conflicts with the performers' relative positions as seen in shot. Instead, the speech should be recorded as from 'centre-stage'. To achieve this, the signals from the two microphones are fed to the camcorder via an audio mixer switched to 'mono' (that is not 'stereo') output.

A creative use for a pair of extension microphones used for recording location sound in stereo is to position one of them to concentrate on the foreground sound, leaving the pick-up of more general background sound to the other microphone. This will add a real feeling of 'audio depth' to the recording. If these two signals differ too much in level, you will need to balance them up at the mixer before passing them on to the camcorder. This is best done by monitoring the signals on headphones, worn perhaps by an assistant.

11 Taping talking heads

Television has been described as 'radio with pictures', and with some justification since we spend much of our viewing time watching and listening to 'talking heads'. News programmes, chat-shows and quizzes are but three examples of the many hours of programming which consist of people talking either to us or to each other. It is no doubt partly a question of economics. As a way of filling schedules, programmes like these are much cheaper to produce then drama and other high cost forms of screen entertainment. On the other hand, talking heads are genuinely popular. Viewers enjoy listening to people who have something interesting to say, and the fact that they can be seen as well as heard adds to the attraction.

Happily, this is one branch of the art of creative video in which amateurs can compete on more equal terms with the professionals. The technical requirements are not too demanding, and telegenic performers can be found in all walks of life. The main task of the producer, in fact, is to make the camera as invisible as possible so that the subjects can relax and come over on the screen just the way they are.

Interviewing Children

To make a beginning, you need look no further than your own family for subjects, your children for example. Maybe you could simply tape them for your memory file, or perhaps you would like to send the recording to relatives who are too far away to keep in touch more directly.

For this kind of recording session, the simpler the set-up the better. If the subjects are to be young children in the company of one or two adults, they could be grouped together on a settee directly facing the camera. This should be positioned so as to include them all in shot at wide angle; you can then zoom in from here for closer shots of individuals. The camcorder should prefer-ably be supported on a tripod at subject eye-level, and the recording done by available light if at all possible. The camcorder's built-in microphone could be used, but it is important to record the speech clearly and an extension mike would no doubt do a better job.

Seat your subjects so that they can turn and speak to each other easily and naturally; this will help them forget about the camera and get on with the conversation, preferably with one member acting as anchorman/woman to keep it going and see fair play. If the tape is intended to be a 'video letter', individuals could be prompted to speak to the camera directly: 'Hello, Auntie Doris, our class won at football today....', and so on.

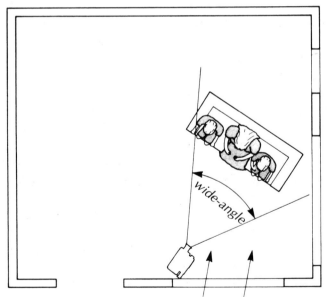

For this kind of set-up, use a tripod if possible, and set the camcorder at a distance which allows the whole zoom range to be used from the one position.

Video Letters

Letters of any kind are all the better for a little thinking in advance about what is to be said, and video-letters are no exception. Before the button is pressed, therefore, the anchorman or anchorwoman should help the group to get its act together by priming individuals with topics to start things off, and prepare to open the recording with a few words of greeting spoken to camera.

Young children will usually co-operate in a recording session with a little encouragement. One good tactic is to introduce favourite toys or books as conversation starters; with any luck, they will soon forget about the camera and just be themselves. Older children tend to be too self-conscious to behave naturally in front of a camera, but may be induced to talk among themselves about school, hobbies and other interests. Adults vary in their ability to perform for video, but one good talker can usually spur on the others sufficiently to promote a reasonably balanced conversation.

Begin the recording with all the participants included in a medium shot and hold this until the discussion begins to warm up, after which you can zoom gently in on whoever is doing most of the talking. From here, your job as camera operator is to follow the talk as it passes from one speaker to another without the camera moves becoming fussy and obtrusive. Panning directly from one person to another in close-up can be tricky: there is always the risk that you will overshoot or arrive at your next close-up just as the person stops speaking. Uncertain and wobbly pans are to be avoided, and a safer option is to pull back from close-up to mid-shot, hold it for a time and then gently zoom back in on the subject for the next close-up.

For a recording of this type, you should use cuts sparingly because they work against the 'real time' feeling which is important for talking heads – any impression that parts have been edited out reduces its value as a human document. Cuts can, however, be made now and then to give your subjects a breathing space if the action begins to flag. If you can, cut between close-shots of different people rather than on mid-shots of the whole group, so that jump-cuts are avoided.

Tidy endings are not always easy to contrive for open ended conversation pieces, and unless you have some kind of pre-arranged way in which to sign off the recording you are liable to end it with everyone conversationally exhausted, glancing at the camera to see if it is still running. A video letter can of course close with goodbyes led by the anchorman/woman. Family memory-tape recordings tend to end in a more indeterminate manner, and the actual point at which to conclude the recording and end on a high note is often best chosen later after the whole session has been played back.

A different form of video letter is to produce an edited compilation of talking heads and family newsreel material. The various sections can be recorded in the final order by editing in camera, or they can be pre-recorded and assemble edited onto a copy tape; a touch of professionalism can be added, if you like, by having a family member act as presenter to introduce each item and link everything together. An obvious advantage of editing onto a copy is that you can select the best material, and you are also able to retain all the original recordings.

Family Newsreels

Family newsreels are fun to shoot. Camcorders with autofocus make it easy to record mobile subjects in and about the house and, within the limits of the available light, you can follow the activities of your family wherever the action takes you. This newsreel style of material, provided that your household accepts candid camera filming as one of the hazards of family life, can provide an excellent contrast to the more static talk sequences, and it gives you the opportunity to preserve for posterity lots of interesting little scenes that you might otherwise have missed. 'Walking' a camcorder while recording does require some practise, however. It is easy to bump into furniture and other obstacles, and there is a 'Groucho lope' which you need to acquire to give mobile shots the necessary minimum of smoothness. As with all hand-held shooting, work the camcorder lens at or near to full wide angle.

Street Interviews

Talking heads can be video taped on the street as well as in the home. Street interviews are in fact yet another facet of creative video. Sometimes they are undertaken in association with a community project or some other local issue. You could for example, arrange to interview your town councillor or local authority representative at a location of interest.

Clearly, you will need to prepare as much as you can in advance for an assignment of this kind so that you can launch into the interview with the minimum of delay once you have got the VIP in your viewfinder. If it is to be on the street, choose a position which will not be an obstruction to the traffic and/or the public, particularly if you are working the camcorder on a tripod. If the interview is to be conducted off the street, say on a supermarket forecourt, it is not only courteous but necessary to clear this with the owners of the property first. Check also that the light will be coming from a favourable direction at the time of day arranged for the shoot.

Interviews at street level make good video, but the close proximity of the public may present problems for the interviewee and camera crew – though it can be surprising how little notice is taken of such activities by the passers-by. As an alternative, however, you may prefer a location much favoured by television news teams, that is a roof-top which overlooks the point of interest. The upper levels of multi-storey car parks, for instance, can provide ideal locations for interviews.

The camera team should consist of camcorder operator and interviewer as a minimum, plus a sound assistant if possible. A hand-microphone is used by the interviewer, who puts the questions and to whom the interviewee addresses the replies. Generally, the camera is aimed over the interviewer's shoulder to give a three-quarters frontal view of the interviewee. The interviewer turns to the camera at the beginning of the session to make the introductions, after which the shot concentrates on the interviewee until the end is reached, whereupon the interviewer turns back to the camera and winds up the session.

'Vox-pop' street interviews take the camera-team back down to street level to accost the passers-by for their views on particular issues. The team must be fully mobile and capable of springing into action whenever a likely subject appears. The interviewer should radiate confidence, smile, and keep to topics of a kind which will provoke an immediate response without the need for lengthy preliminary explanations. Questions which allow a single 'yes' or 'no' in reply should be avoided. Instead, put them in the form of 'What do you think of ...?' to encourage a more revealing response. If the same question is to be repeated for each interview, it need only be heard in full the first time, after which it can be edited out when the final version is being assembled.

Formal Interviews

Interviews of a more formal and lengthy character can make good viewing provided, of course, that the subject has something interesting to say and can put it over in an entertaining manner. If the subject is articulate, the interview element can be used as a means

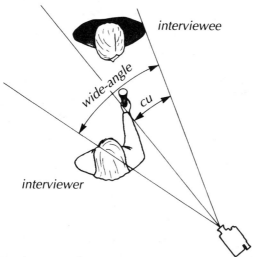

Make sure that your chosen on-camera interview position works for both the wide-angle shots and the close-ups before you start the shoot. Use a tripod.

of introducing the personality to the viewers, after which he or she can be left to get on with it with only the minimum of prompting.

You may be lucky enough to find someone who is able to recall aspects of bygone local life and customs which are in danger of being lost to future generations if they are not recorded while the opportunity still offers. There are many tales from the past which are worth telling, and video can play a vital role in preserving this part of our heritage. It is good, therefore, to seek such people out and get them onto tape; perhaps there is a historical society in your area which would be glad to cooperate with you on this.

For such an interview, the setting could be an outdoor one if appropriate, but indoors is generally the best place for this kind of work. Planning is often easier, there are no uncertainties about the weather, and the interviewee will probably be more relaxed, especially if the recording is made on his or her home ground. If possible, shoot in available light, in window daylight for example, but don't hesitate to bring in extra lighting if need be, preferably bounce lighting (see page 120). These are important recordings and should be shot to the highest standards. You should also take trouble to produce a good sound recording. It is essential that the speech should be clear and recorded without intrusive background noise. Interviewer and interviewee should preferably wear tie-clip microphones, and the team should include a sound assistant whose sole job is to make sure that all the audio equipment is functioning correctly and that the signal levels are satisfactory.

The camcorder will be tripod-mounted and aimed over the interviewer's shoulder in the three-quarters frontal arrangement (see page 145). Plan in advance how the opening introduction is to be made. If the interviewer is to do this in the form of speech direct to camera, it should be recorded separately as a reverse-shot, preferably just before the interview itself begins. This may require special lighting arrangements, and the opportunity should then be taken to record some 'noddies', that is reaction shots which can be edited-in to hide jump-cuts at breaks in the recording. These might be close-ups of the interviewer nodding, smiling, looking keenly interested and so on. They can also be used as inserts (over which the speech in the main shot continues) if it is felt necessary to edit in additional visual variety.

Before the main session begins, settle everyone in their places and make sure that the subject knows what questions to expect. Have the sound assistant pre-check the microphone levels first and then get the recording under way without haste but also without unnecessary delay. Keeping the interviewee waiting while technical snags are ironed out is a sure way to spoil the session before it even starts.

The recording could open with a speech to camera beginning something like: 'George Brown has taken a keen interest in local history for many years, and...,' at the end of which the interviewer's eye-line switches from direct-to-camera to the (off-screen) interviewee, cut to the latter; the interviewer continues: 'George, I know that you are pretty knowledgeable on the subject of... tell us something about it.' George begins to speak, looking past the camera at the off-screen interviewer. At the end of the session, the interviewer wraps up the recording in some suitable way, either in reverse-shot or as an off-screen thank you.

Life Stories

There is another approach to the taping of interesting people and their life stories, and this is to have them speak directly to camera without interviewer. Not many people are capable of holding the screen on their own in this way, but if you happen to hit on someone with such a talent, don't fail to make good use of this golden opportunity.

Heads talking directly to camera can be recorded in domestic and other real life settings. Alternatively, you could consider providing a simple studio background. This has much to recommend it because it helps to concentrate the viewer's attention on the speaker without irrelevant visual distraction. This time, the camera is set square-on the subject at a distance which allows the full zoom range to be used from close-up to medium shot or beyond. This one viewpoint is going to cover the whole recording, so the range of shot size available therefore needs to be on the generous side.

Since the subject will not have the benefit of promptings by an interviewer, a prompt-board may be needed to provide simple reminders of subject headings, key phrases, or even to give the speech to camera in full. Prompt-boards can be made up from large sheets of paper attached to hard-board, and written out in felt-tip pen. The lettering should be big enough to be readable when the boards are held close to the camera. One difficulty with prompt-boards is that they shift the subject's eye-line away from the camera lens, and this can be very noticeable in close-shots especially if the eye can be seen moving over the lines and from top to the bottom of the sheet. A compromise has to be made, therefore, between the size of the sheet and hence its readability, and getting as much of the lettering as close in to the lens as possible.

For this kind of single-subject recording, the camera zooming needs to be done with an ultra-light touch and as slowly as possible. It may in fact need to be done by hand if the power zoom speed on your camcorder is too fast. Start the recording with the subject in medium shot as he or she begins to speak, and hold this until the session has had time to get properly under way. Then, gradually ease the zoom in, a stage at a time, to finally arrive at a close-shot just as the first key point in the narrative is reached (this pre-supposes that you have been briefed before-hand on what is going to be said). Having held the close-shot for a time, you then relieve the tension by zooming back first to medium close-up and then perhaps back to medium shot ready for the visual build-up towards the next key point.

Avoid the trap of zooming, even very slowly, all of the time. Have the courage to let the shot rest at each setting until you judge that the time is ripe to change the shot to one which is either a little closer or a little wider. Err on the side of caution: it is all too easy to spoil a recording with misjudged and unnecessary camera moves, and to ask for a retake is likely to make things even worse – the first take is often the best for sessions like these.

One possible camera arrangement for taping a group discussion; another would be to dispense with the table and seat the group in a half-circle with the camera at the centre.

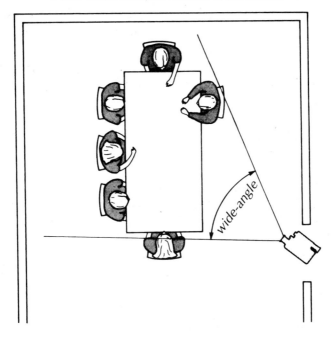

If, for any reason, a mistake is made or the subject 'dries' and it becomes necessary to break the recording to allow a restart part of the way through, the interruption can be hidden at editing by the insertion of a photograph or some relevant piece of artwork. These forced stoppages can sometimes be a blessing in disguise as they necessitate the editing in of additional visual interest, but inserts can of course be added where appropriate even if there are no jump-cuts to hide.

Group Interviews

The recording of groups of talking heads – meetings, discussions and so on – is another challenge that you may be called on to tackle as a video maker. The groups may be large or small, seated in rows or in a circle, and under the control of a leader or under no control at all.

If the group is in charge of a leader, things are much simpler. He or she provides the anchor which holds the proceedings together, and the microphone problem is also solved: the leader can be put in charge of a roving hand-mike which can either be a cable-connected type or, for added convenience and reduced handling noise, a radio microphone can be used. The group then sits in one or more rows facing the camera, and the leader begins by introducing the group and its topic of discussion to the viewers, following this with contributions from individual members of the group in turn and ending the session with a closing speech to camera.

Given a competent leader, nobody is allowed to monopolise the discussion, and the camera operator simply follows his or her lead. If mobility is called for, the camera can be hand-held news-reel fashion, an arrangement which makes it easier to keep the field of view clear of the leader's comings and goings.

For the alternative and less camera-friendly group without a leader, the discussion is likely to range in a random and unplanned fashion from one individual to another, and there is no set format to help the camera operator who therefore has to follow the action as best he can.

The members of the group need to be able to make eye contact with each other, and a half-circular seating arrangement is then more appropriate. The camera is mounted on a tripod placed at the centre of the arc and at a height which is about that of the eye-level of the participants, some of whom may be sitting on the floor. The scene should be evenly illuminated so that no one is sitting in shadow, and available lighting or bounce should be used.

The unpredictability of the action makes things quite exciting for both camera and sound crews. The camera operator often will not know which person to fix on from one moment to the next, and will sometimes be left high and dry as the discussion moves about. If this happens to you, don't pan the camera in a desperate attempt to catch up: stay with your chosen close-up, win or lose, in the hope that the person in shot will at least be reacting to what is being said off-camera. If a second camera is available, this can be used as a back-up to provide cutaway alternatives for insertion at the editing stage.

The sound recordist, on the other hand, must find a way of following the sound with the microphone. The obvious choice for a job like this is to use a boom-mounted mike, there being no leader to handle a hand-microphone and assuming that the group is too large to be provided with personal mikes for each member. The boom operator should take up a position to the rear of the camera so that the microphone can be swung over everyone's head and hopefully not appear in shot. As an alternative, one or more omnidirectional microphones can be set up on stands in front of the group. The signals from these are fed to a mixer operated by the sound assistant who adjusts the levels to suit. However, the success of this method may be compromised by the room acoustics if these are boomy, as it may be impossible to place the microphones close enough in to the speakers to swamp the echoes.

12 Taping a wedding

W eddings bring out the photographer in all of us, and the appearance of the happy couple on the church steps is nowadays accompanied by a perfect crescendo of camera-clicking. In recent years, the video recording of weddings has also come to be an accepted part of the wedding ritual, and the sight of a camcorder at work among the well-wishers is now commonplace. The taping of weddings is an established business activity in its own right, and the official stills photographer no longer has the monopoly over the wedding photography.

Although the recording of a wedding might seem to be a fairly straightforward task, it is in reality quite a challenging assignment if a full record is to be made which is worthy of the occasion. Whether done for pleasure or profit, wedding videos need to be carefully planned if they are not to end in disappointment for the people whose day it is. However, weddings are themselves occasions which are generally preplanned months in advance, so if you have been asked to be responsible for making the video recording, there should be no shortage of information on which to base your own plans.

Advance Planning

Weddings proceed in four distinct stages: the arrivals at church; the ceremony; the photo-call after the ceremony; and the reception. The first thing to do is to establish in advance exactly what is expected of you. Is the recording to be limited to the scenes outside the church before and after the service – or is the ceremony to be included? If so, has the officiating clergyman given permission for this to be done? Is the reception to be covered? If so, which parts? For instance, should it include shots of the guests arriving and being received by the bride and groom, or should

This is the kind of layout you should have in your mind's eye when planning the exteriors for a church wedding shoot. Camera position (1) covers the arrivals for the service, while (2) is the basic position for the photo-call after the ceremony. Additional positions can be found on the day to enable you to add variety to the coverage.

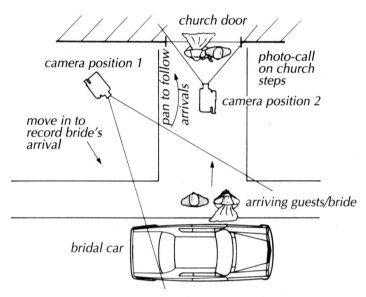

only the speeches and cutting the cake be recorded? If there is to be a party after the meal, is this to be covered also? Although these may seem to be obvious points to make, it is vital that you reach a clear understanding of them from the outset.

Next, sort out the video format on which the tape is to be produced. This should either be the same format as your camcorder, or if not, you will need to arrange to run a copy. In any case, the running of a copy has the advantage that it enables you to retain the original as an insurance against loss of, or damage to, the copy as well as allowing you to edit out any unsatisfactory shots before you hand it over. Furthermore, if the original is being shot on VHS-C, the possible inconvenience of the short runtimes of these cassettes can be overcome by copying them onto a full-size cassette. If, on the other hand, you intend to hand over VHS-C originals, check that the recipient appreciates that an adapter is needed to allow them to be played on a full-size VHS machine. Do not shoot VHS-C at LP (half speed) unless the recipient has access to a two-speed machine on which to play the material back!

The shooting of the scenes outside the church should present no technical problems unless it happens to be raining, a contingency which you should plan for in advance. Camcorders must not be operated in wet weather unless they are adequately protected, so at the very least you should organise an assistant to hold an umbrella over both you and the machine if the need arises. Better and more reliable protection can be given to the camcorder by purchasing one of the special weatherproof enclosures which are now available. (Some camcorders are available in fully weatherproofed versions.)

Rather more effort has to be put into the preplanning for recording the service and the reception. The question of permission has already been referred to. This should be no problem for the reception; the owners of the premises on which these are generally held are usually quite happy to allow not only the photography but also the use of special lighting if required – but ask them first.

In contrast, church clergy are sometimes understandably reluctant to permit photography of any kind during their services, and where permission to record is granted this is usually with the proviso that only the normal church lighting can be used. It is therefore prudent to check on the level of that lighting before you commit to recording the wedding service. However, if your camcorder is a recent low-light model, you should be able to produce pictures of some kind even if the lighting is poor, as it is in many churches.

Camera Position

Another important point which you need to agree in advance is the camera position to be used in church. The best position is usually close to the altar-rail and angled towards the place where the couple will stand to make their vows; it should be possible to cover the bride's walk to the altar from here, and also the couple's departure to sign the register. If you are really close in, you should be able to pick up the responses adequately on the camcorder's built-in microphone as well as the rest of the service.

In the event that this position is considered to be too obtrusive, you may have to settle for an alternative – perhaps on a balcony – which is further away and from which it is not possible to pick up the altar responses clearly enough. In this case, you should seek permission to use an extension microphone placed near the altar. Whichever position that you choose or are offered, be sure to check that there are no windows in the background of the field of view to give problems with backlighting.

While you are on this preliminary visit to the church, take the opportunity to have a look outside. On the day, the main task before the service is to ensure that all the key people are included on the recording as they arrive. Choose vantage points from which to take the guests as they approach the church, and from which the arrival of the bridal car can be recorded. Finally, it is a nice idea to take a long shot view of the church itself to begin the video, so pick a spot from which this can be taken on the day, bearing in mind the direction the light will be coming from at the time in question.

A quick inspection of the room in which the reception is to be held is also time well spent. If you can, get an idea of the intended table layout in relation to the lighting – does the top table face towards or away from window daylight? If windows are likely to present a backlight problem, can curtains be drawn? If you plan to use video lights, where are the nearest power sockets?

Shooting the Arrivals

On the day, be sure that you arrive at the church early. The first job is to record the view of the church. Start the tape with a few seconds of blank black to get the recording off to a businesslike start. First impressions are important, so mount the camcorder on a tripod and take care over the lining up of the shot to make it as attractive as you can. Also, if a title is to be superimposed in-camera by character-generator, this opening shot is the one on which it should be done. Give yourself plenty of time to complete these preliminaries.

Once outside the church itself, make yourself known to the usher on the door, and secure his help in identifying the guests if these are not already known to you. When the stills photographer appears on the scene, establish friendly and non-competitive relations, there is no need for you to get in each other's way.

In a well-conducted wedding, the groom and the best man will also be at the church early, and are probably to be found nervously waiting by the door for the first guests. This is your opportunity to take a few candid camera shots of these two while things are relatively quiet. The best man can probably be persuaded to display the ring, which would make a nice shot.

As the guests begin to arrive, get to your pre-arranged camera position and prepare for a busy half-hour. Anyone wearing a button-hole is fair game, but at all costs be sure to get a flattering shot of the bride's mother. Concentrate on getting nice steady shots as the people walk past to the door, and try to introduce variety (and reduce the effect of any jump-cuts) by frequent changes of shot size. Also, allow some guests to walk right past and out of shot, but pan to follow others as they continue along the church path; cut, of course, before you pan back for the next arrivals.

As the time for the service approaches, onlookers will begin to gather, and, if time allows, you can take one or two quick close-ups of these to cut into the shots of the arrivals. Turning heads and a sudden hush will herald the approach of the car with the bridesmaids and, after a suitable interval, the bride. The stills photographer will no doubt be taking pictures of the bride as she leaves the car, and this is your cue to follow suit, after which you need to get back to your position outside the door for one of the most important shots in the whole recording: the bride's approach and entry into the church.

You now have to move very rapidly to your camera position inside for another key shot, the bride's arrival at the altar. Hopefully, you will have been able to arrange for her to pause for a moment or two at the door to give you sufficient time in which to make this move. If you take too long, she and the organist will beat you to it and the Wedding March will have already begun before you can get the recording under way again.

The Ceremony

Wedding ceremonies take an average of about twenty minutes from beginning to end, and it is customary to record the whole service without a break. This is done for the sake of completeness

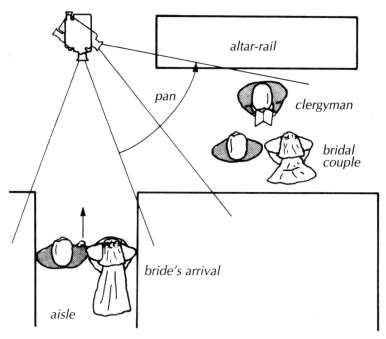

Ideally, one camera position will cover both the bride's arrival at the altar and the marriage ceremony itself. Make occasional zooms to wide-angle in order to include the congregation. Use a tripod and record the ceremony in full without breaks.

and also to avoid any awkward jump-cuts in the sound, especially on music. Since there will be no opportunities to make a battery change during the service, you should ensure that the one in the camcorder starts the recording of the ceremony with sufficient charge remaining unless, as is preferable, you are running on mains for this part of the recording. To be on the safe side, take at least one fully charged spare battery with you.

Twenty minutes is much too long a time to hold a camcorder with reasonable steadiness, and the use of a tripod is strongly recommended. From this shooting position, you should be able to zoom in to the medium and close-up views of the group at the altar, and also be able to zoom out to wider angles in order to include the congregation. For the most part, though, you should hold the shot steadily on the couple and let the picture tell its own story without interruption.

After the register has been signed, a proceeding which you may have been asked to include on the video, you have to get outside again as quickly as you can to be in place to cover the appearance of the newly-weds on the church steps. The photo-call will be held either here or in some nearby location, and this part of the affair will very definitely be under the direction of the stills photographer whose lead you will need to follow. Don't be too worried if things start to become a chaotic muddle as people mill around chatting and forming into various groups to have their pictures taken. This is all part of the wedding atmosphere, and your own shots can reflect this. They can be quite short, and taken with a mobile camera in all kinds of different shot sizes and angles. Try to keep away from the church door if the organ is audible so that the jump-cuts in the sound will not be noticeable. Get plenty of close-ups of the two families for the video album, and be sure to be in the thick of the confetti when it begins to fly as the couple leave for the reception.

The Reception

Getting the camcorder to the reception ahead of the wedding car is another of those races against time which you have to win, so have your own transport waiting in readiness. The arrival of the guests at the reception is yet another opportunity to record them for posterity, so set up by the door and keep the camcorder running until the flow of arrivals ceases. From the video point of view, there now comes something of a lull, and there is little for you to do until the meal nears its end and the speeches begin. Form an alliance with the best man here, and arrange a system of winks and nods whereby he can signal you to switch on just before he raps on the table and calls for order.

The recording of the speeches is another job which calls for a little technical finesse. Hopefully, you will have been able to set up an extension microphone (and possibly lights) in front of the top table in advance. The camera position should be one in which you get good three-quarter profiles of the speakers and also a good view of the cutting of the cake. In between times, you can go for one or two close shots of the guests.

Wedding Video Check List

- *View of the church.*
- *Bridegroom and best man.*
- *Guests arriving at the church.*
- *Arrival of the bridesmaids.*
- *Arrival of the bride.*
- *Bride's arrival at the altar.*
- *The ceremony.*
- *Signing the register.*
- *Newly-weds on the church steps.*
- *Groups of relatives.*
- *Arrival of guests at the reception.*
- *Recording of speeches.*
- *Cutting of the cake.*

Beginning and Endings

There are various ways in which your wedding video can be brought to a close. One is to fade out on a two-shot of the bride and groom as the reception comes to an end. Another is to follow them to the car as they leave for their honeymoon. Whatever kind of ending you opt for, it should be in keeping with the rest of the video and tie it up neatly. You may want to add an end title which can be edited in before the tape is handed over.

There are other ways of beginning the video, too. For instance, it could start by showing the final preparations at the home of the bride, and even her departure for church. If the tape is to be post-production assemble edited, it makes it possible to combine material shot on more than one camera, and the difficulties of trying to be in two places at once are greatly reduced. Shots from a variety of sources and locations can be intercut to build fully-edited sequences, and jump-cuts in both pictures and sound can be completely eliminated.

However you tackle the taping of a wedding, one thing is certain: weddings proceed at their own pace irrespective of the needs of camcorders and their operators, and there can be no retakes! Even so, they are well within the scope of camcorder enthusiasts, and are a wonderful way of preserving the memories of a unique occasion.

Taping sports and pastimes

I f you are a sports enthusiast, you will need no convincing that sport is a natural subject for the small screen. Games, and outdoor activities in general, though, are covered with such smooth professionalism on television that it seems almost a waste of time for amateurs, with their puny resources, to attempt any kind of sports coverage of their own.

Football

The value of what can be done at amateur level depends, of course, on what is intended. The coverage of large scale sporting events such as league football requires multi-camera set-ups working through vision mixers. This is beyond the scope of most amateurs and even video clubs, but if the scale is reduced, say, to amateur football, and the aim is to produce a single-camera record of a match for the benefit of the players and their supporters, the practical possibilities immediately become apparent. All that you then need is a camcorder and a vantage point from which you can cover the field of play.

Although you could simply stand on the touch-line and take your shots from ground level, ideally you need to be raised up a metre or so and positioned a little back from the edge of the pitch. You are then clear of spectators who might otherwise block your view, and you can angle your shots downwards onto the players. Apart from giving you a better angle, the higher position also reduces the amount of sky in the picture and hence minimises problems with backlighting. The back of a pickup truck makes a good camera platform and provides a solid base from which to operate. If you have the use of one of these, try to position it so that you will be shooting with the light rather than against it.

If you are keen on the game, you will find that video taping a whole match is quite absorbing but requires almost as much stamina as it does to be a player. As you follow the play, you should try to anticipate the roll of the ball and keep the centre of the picture slightly ahead of it. Use the zoom to control the picture size to compensate for changes in distance as the play moves about on the pitch, and keep the field of view as wide as possible but not so wide that the details of the game are lost. This calls for deft finger-work on the zoom buttons. Too many telephoto close-ups of kicking feet are tiring to watch and tell little of the game as a whole.

If your intention, though, is simply to produce a newsreel of highlights of the game rather than a continuous recording, you can move about the touch-line with a mobile camera, or even two cameras. Your coverage could include crowd reaction shots which, provided that the eyelines of the spectators match the direction, can be used as cutaways to bridge jump-cuts in the play. If two camcorders are available, one could be assigned to cover the game as a whole from a fixed high-angle position, while the other could be given a roving commission to go for close-up details of highlights and spectator reactions. The mobile material could later be assembled or inserted into the master recording as appropriate to provide a budget version of professional multi-camera coverage. You could give some extra polish to your production by adding a running commentary, dubbed *ad lib* during the transfer of the original recording onto a copy tape.

Tennis

Tennis is a game which is much easier to cover with a single camcorder: tennis courts are much smaller than football pitches, and the pattern of play is more predictable. It can therefore be covered from a camera position looking directly down the court from behind one of the players, but set high enough up and far enough back to do justice to both. Again, if a second camera is being used, this can be assigned to pick up the spectator reactions for insertion into the master tape, though the to-and-fro head movements of the onlookers – which should synchronise with the play as heard over the original sound – make the timing of inserts rather tricky to pull off successfully. For the sound, an extension microphone should be positioned close to the net, so that the thud of ball on racquet can be clearly heard, and commentary can be added either live while the game is being recorded or later at editing stage.

Snooker

Snooker makes a colourful subject for video, and, of all games, it is probably the easiest one to cover with a single camera which can be set to look down the centre line of the table. The pace of snooker tournaments is usually so leisurely that even the most tongue-tied of commentators should have no difficulty in keeping up with the play. The table should be well-lit, otherwise the depth of field may be rather shallow at such a close range, and your autofocus may have a hard time keeping the subject in focus – or even in deciding which of the balls on the table *is* the subject. Hence, you may have to resort to manual focus if the depth of field is insufficient even at wide angle.

The game also lends itself to a more impressionistic camera style as an alternative to a straightforward record of match play. For this, the camera is moved in to the table at eye-level and allowed to dwell on the sensual roll and click of coloured balls on green baize. There is scope here for the use of differential focusing, whereby all but the foreground subject is seen as a hazy blur; there is scope for imaginative editing, too, both of pictures and sound.

Golf

To return from smoke-filled rooms to the wide outdoors, the game of golf has its television followers, and it is covered for broadcast by very elaborate and expensive facilities. Nevertheless, given the co-operation of the players, it is quite possible to cover a game with a single mobile camera if the greens are not too busy.

Golf is a socially oriented game and the pace of it is slow enough to allow the camera to seek out close-up studies revealing the different characters of the players as they drive off into the rough and miss easy putts. Unlike most other sports, in fact, golf can be shot in much the same way as any ordinary movie with shot sizes ranging from wide-angle establishers showing the fairway from the point of view of the players, to mid-shots and close-ups as they approach the holes. You can even indulge in some parallel-action intercutting of the players as they settle down to business on the green.

If you can muster an interviewer and a sound assistant with gun-microphone, you can try your hand at recording chat between holes provided, that is, you can walk the camera back-wards. At a simpler technical level, you can take your camcorder to professional tournaments where the chance of a good telephoto shot of a celebrity might spur you on.

Golf-swing analysis gives video yet another opportunity to prove its worth on the golf course, and it also justifies the use of a 'high speed shutter' or a 'sports' AE program, if you have such a facility on your camcorder, to boost the shutter to a higher rate than its normal 1/50th of a second to 1/5000th or more. This has the effect of 'freezing' the motion of rapidly moving objects such as the swing of golf clubs, converting what is seen on normally shot single-frames as a blur, into a series of sharply defined images. This enables the details of the stroke to be examined, either in slow-motion or frame by frame, provided the playback machine has matching high-speed characteristics.

High-speed shutter can be used in a similar way for such things as racing cars and horses, and for studies of high speed machinery. However, its desirability for normal recording is debatable because the very sharpness of the definition tends to make moving objects look rather unreal, a blurred image being closer to what we perceive with the naked eye. Also, the faster shutter speed involves a corre-sponding reduction in the exposure, so the camcorder lens has to work at a wider aperture to compensate for this. Therefore, the facility is suitable for use only in well-lit conditions.

School Sports

If golf is a club activity, a school sports day is a social occasion. A full record of such an event will devote as much time to the socialising as to the prowess of the athletes. The camera should be mobile, wide-ranging, and used to capture as much of the atmosphere of the event as possible. This is another situation where two camcorders are better then one; they can operate independently within an overall plan of campaign, and the best of both tapes can be assemble edited together afterwards.

To record such events as sprint races, a good camera position is one which looks diagonally across the course towards the start line so that you can pan with the leading runners as they go by to the finish. If a second camera can be at the finish line, so much the better. An effective way of using it is to mount it on a tripod and have it looking up the course on telephoto. As the runners approach, gradually zoom out to end on full wide angle so that the competitors will surge past in impressive style. Concentrate on taking plenty of close-ups of the spectators cheering the runners on and applauding the winners, not forgetting to make sure of a good camera position for the speeches and the presentation of prizes at the end of the day.

Water Events

Swimming events require a similar camera technique. Indoor pools do present special problems, though, one being the headache of condensation which readily forms in such moisten-laden spaces. To minimise the risk of a steamed-up lens, allow your equipment to acclimatise to the different air temperature, and if your lens does steam up, wipe it gently with a special lens cleaning tissue. If the humidity is really high, your camcorder's dew detector may activate and switch off the machine, which will then be unusable until the condition has cleared; this may take some time. Condensation is a major hazard to video equipment, and it is better not to risk electrical damage or jamming of the head mechanism by attempting to use it in damp conditions unless it is properly protected.

If your camcorder is fully enclosed in a pressure-tight container or is one which is inherently sealed against incoming water, you can even take it with you when you go skin-diving. Underwater shots of marine life have a fascination and a beauty all of their own, and taping them is an absorbing activity. The clarity of your under-water shots will of course be dependent on the clarity of the water; any cloudiness not only reduces general visibility but also the penetration of the daylight and effectiveness of any artificial lights you may be using. Water-skiing is another exciting use for fully water-proofed video equipment and can bring a new meaning to the term 'mobile camera'.

Winter Sports

Winter sports offer quite a different environment for making video recordings, one of the challenges being the operation of the equipment in cold conditions. Most camcorders are specified to be used in air temperatures not lower than 0°C (32°F), and may give trouble if used unprotected in a severe frost. Be on your guard for condensation if you take your camcorder straight from a warm room into cold outside air; allow time for it to adjust to the lower temperature before you begin to use it. As far as choice of subject goes, you can hardly go wrong at a skiing resort. Everyone is wearing bright colours, there is plenty of action both expert and novice, and the ski-lifts provide ideal camera platforms from which to take dramatic tracking shots of the scenery going by below. These can take on an almost three-dimensional quality.

Sunlight on snow can provide magnificent photographic opportunities if handled correctly. Go for scenes which are cross-lit and with the sun at a fairly low angle so that the background will be thrown into strong relief and not appear simply as a dazzling and featureless expanse of white. This also helps to reduce the contrast between the snow and the faces of skiers in the foreground which will otherwise come out too dark because of the backlight effect; if necessary, apply backlight correction in the usual way. If the conditions are very bright, they may exceed the working limits of your automatic exposure control system and you then have an over-exposure problem. The answer is to fit a neutral density filter over the camcorder lens; this will cut down the amount of light entering the lens by several stops and thus solve the difficulty.

Aerial Shooting

If you are really adventurous, you can take to the air and go microlight flying, gliding or ballooning with your camcorder, but check your insurance cover for both man and machine first! Apart from the aerial shots, there are all the ground activities to cover as well: microlight assembly before take-off, glider preparation and balloon inflation are all interesting video subjects in themselves and show the practical background to the poetic business of flight.

The inflation of a hot-air balloon, for instance, is quite an impressive sight. It is, however, a rather slow-motion affair, and you will need to telescope down the time that it really takes by showing just part of each stage of the procedure. You should therefore shoot plenty of cutaways to bridge over the jump-cuts in the action; close-up studies of the enthusiasts absorbed in their tasks make ideal material for filling these gaps. You may also need to smooth away the jumps in the sound at the edits, and the mixing-in of a continuous background effect – which can be woven in and out of the sync sound – may be just what is required. You could record this effect for yourself on a portable sound recorder which could be taken along and left running while you are getting your shots of the inflation process.

The best time to take aerial shots is when the sun is casting long shadows so that the lie of the land can be clearly seen. The shots should be taken from moderate altitude, say 150–300m (500–1000ft), and the attachment of a UV filter to your camcorder lens will help to cut down the atmospheric haze and give your pictures pin-sharp definition. If you can, give some camera time to whoever is flying the balloon with you. Conditions will no doubt be rather cramped, and the use of a wide-angle converter attachment may help you to secure better shots of your companion and also of the panorama below.

You may even be able to record an aerial interview; if not, you should certainly make every effort, once you are safely back on *terra firma*, to get some of the balloonists to share their experiences and enthusiasms for the benefit of the camera. Folk who have a passionate interest in unusual activities are generally worth recording; if they happen to be camera-shy, you could record them on sound only and dub their voices over the relevant sections of the video. Biking and go-karting are two more sports which have their dedicated followers and video can be used to give an insight into these popular pastimes.

Canal Sailing

Barge sailing on the canals is a very peaceful way of getting about, the passage of the locks being the only element of drama in what is otherwise an activity which is somewhat lacking in incident. Nevertheless, canals, barges and the people who sail them can provide good material for video. It is a mode of transport with a long and interesting history, and there is plenty of scope for a documentary approach, perhaps combined with the story of a particular cruise. There are all kinds of aspects to the working of a canal from the operation of locks to the life-styles of people who spend most of their leisure time moving up and down the waterways at walking pace, the 'put-put-put' of the engine making a suitable accompaniment as the canal banks glide slowly past.

Technically, a project such as this is not too demanding, the only real problem being the recharging of the camcorder battery *en route*. However, every canal has its series of traditional pubs whose landlords can usually be persuaded to let you plug your battery-charger into the power supply for an hour or so.

Railway Documentary

A day on a preservation steam railway is another fruitful subject for video. Line-side shots of a steam locomotive in full cry make magnificent moving pictures, and the leisurely rituals of station operation make an effective contrast to the roar and rattle of

passing trains. If you have brought family or friends with you, here
is a proposed plan of action for a video of the day:

Steam Railway Narrative

- *Arrive at the station and go out onto the platform to await the train.*
- *A distant whistle is heard, and heads turn to look up the line.*
- *The station signal changes to green (a close-up, so you can hear the clank as it operates).*
- *The train comes slowly into view and draws into the station.*
- *From your camera position at the end of the platform, you have a good view of the locomotive as it blows off steam.*
- *Along the platform, excited children are scrambling up into the carriages followed by their parents.*
- *The engine is being uncoupled by the fireman while the driver and two small boys look on.*
- *Carriage doors are slammed, and heads pop out of windows.*
- *The engine slowly trundles by on the loop-line to the other end of the train.*
- *A last-minute passenger arrives and gets on board.*
- *The engine is recoupled and the guard is waiting to give the 'off'.*
- *On the train, the family is now settling down for the ride.*
- *Through the window, the guard's whistle is answered by the engine, and the train begins to move out of the station . . .*

Another way into the subject might be to look at it from the
technical or historical viewpoint through the eyes of a railway
enthusiast. This releases you from the restraints of showing a

particular journey and allows you to concentrate instead on other aspects such as the types of locos and rolling stock in use on the line, or how the line is being operated by volunteers under today's conditions. If you are not knowledgeable yourself on these matters, you will obviously have to seek the help of those who are, and you should in any case obtain permission from the railway society whose line it is before you embark on any major project which involves their operations.

Drama

The video taping of drama is a large subject, and there is space here only to sketch in the main possibilities. The first decision to be made is whether the drama is to be shot as a theatrical production, or whether it is to be produced and recorded in non-theatrical settings such as ordinary domestic interiors, or outdoors. For instance, a simple drama could be shot in your home and/or garden, the cast being drawn from members of your family or friends.

Technically, the requirements can be modest. For a single-camera shoot, the shots can be set up and lit individually one at a time using either bounce or three-lamp lighting arrangements, and the sound can be recorded from either a single boom-microphone or concealed radio mikes worn by each of the actors. The production can be edited in camera if preferred, but it is probably more practical to shoot it for assemble editing onto a copy tape later, a method which enables the director to shoot as many takes as he or she likes of each scene, leaving the selection of the best material to be done at the editing stage.

If the drama is to be, say, a domestic comedy of your own devising, a script will first have to be prepared. Start by writing down the plot in the form of a brief summary. This is known as a treatment, and its purpose is to get the main thrust of the story clear in everyone's mind. It is followed by the preparation of a more detailed screenplay in which the actions, dialogue and stage directions are set out in full. From this, you then work out a shooting script which gives the details of each shot and camera set-up. This is set out on the left hand side of the page, the corresponding lines of dialogue being written down opposite the shots on the right hand side. With this complete, you can then get on with the shooting.

For a more ambitious drama production, you might seek the cooperation of your local drama group, or you may be a member of a video club with access to a wider range of acting talent. Acting for the small screen, though, is very different to acting for the stage, and theatrical performers who are used to projecting their performances to the back of the auditorium often find it difficult to scale down their actions for the camera. Screen close-ups convey emotions and expressions very directly, and bodily gesture has to be kept down to the minimum or it will appear over done on the screen.

Video, however, does have a part to play in the theatre. It is frequently used for recording rehearsals because it allows the actors to study their performances from the audience's viewpoint. Since the recordings are intended only for temporary use, they can be made with the minimum of technical resource and the standard of the recording needs to be no more than adequate. For the taping of an actual performance, however, a higher standard is called for. The way in which this can be achieved depends on whether or not a separate performance, perhaps a dress-rehearsal, can be put on specially for the camera. If it can, this helps matters considerably because the video equipment can be brought right up onto the stage if need be, and the performance can be interrupted as required to allow the camera, together with any special lighting, to be moved around from scene to scene.

If, on the other hand, the recording is to be made in the presence of an audience, it will have to be covered by one or more cameras positioned in the auditorium. If the cameras are operating independently, their recordings may be edited down later to form a composite assembly of the best material from the original tapes. A more professional alternative method of shooting is to feed the camera signals to a vision mixer under the control of a director who edits the video in real time as the recording is made.

The video director will have needed to make a careful study of the script of the play beforehand and have produced from it a camera-shooting script. On this, the angles and moves for each camera are worked out and rehearsed in advance, since the cameras have to keep pace with the action on the stage without any breaks or opportunities for retakes.

Good sound recording technique is also important for this kind of video work, and several microphones should be suspended over the proscenium and connected to an audio mixer under the control of a sound recordist whose job it is to keep the sound in balance as the action moves about the stage. Do not overlook the fact that it is illegal to record a copyright production without permission, and licences to cover the making of such recordings can be obtained from the Mechanical Copyright Protection Society.

Special effects and graphics

Special effects cover a whole range of visual tricks from the simple to the complex. Some are based on optical illusions which have been exploited by film makers ever since the day of the silent cinematograph, while others depend on the latest electronics to manipulate the screen images in all kinds of new ways.

Confusion of Planes

One trick depends on the deliberate confusion of planes in a two-dimensional picture, the comic possibilities of which were put to good use by the earliest film producers. In one classic example, we see the comedian apparently lolling at his ease in the back of an expensive motorcar. As the car pulls away from the kerb, the 'passenger' is left standing on the pavement, where he was all the time. The lack of the depth dimension fooled the audience into thinking that he was actually in the car. This throw-away visual gag appeared in many different versions, and it still amuses audiences today. No special equipment is required to make it work, just a little imagination.

The confusion-of-planes trick can be used to create giants and dwarfs: people placed near to the camera look larger than those who are further away. Given careful attention to the camera angle, and provided that there are no objects in the scene to give clues to the actual scales, the eye will accept the differences in image size as real differences because the flat picture makes the people seem to be closer together than they actually are.

In a similar way, models can be made to look as large as the real thing. Suppose you want to show a flying saucer sitting on

This set-up shows a flying saucer sitting in your back garden. Set a model saucer close to the camcorder leaving the house visible in the background. Because of the distance between saucer and house, the model will appear much larger than it really is. The illusion depends on the fact that video pictures are two-dimensional, and it is important that both model and background are in equally sharp focus. Choose a bright day to do the recording, and set the lens at wide angle so that the depth of field will be maximised.

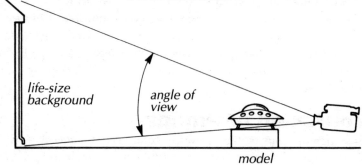

your back lawn. If you have a suitable model, set it up at some distance from the house. The camcorder is then positioned close to it and angled so that the house appears to be dwarfed by it. Carefully arranged, the trick will be quite convincing if the house and saucer are in equally sharp focus. To achieve this you need maximum depth of field, so the shot should be taken on a bright day with the lens set on wide angle. You can include human figures in the background if you like to reinforce the illusion. Take care, though, to check that there are no out-of-scale details in the foreground, such as blades of grass, to give the game away.

Distorted Images

The wide-angle setting on your zoom lens can be used to produce distorted images. If you set the lens to maximum wide angle and place the camcorder close to the subject, the depth of the scene will appear to be greatly exaggerated. Noses project from faces in a most unflattering fashion, and giant hands attached to spindly arms swim in and out of the picture in a weird sort of way. If you combine this effect with high or low camera angles, some very strange and threatening images can be produced. The wider the zoom angle, the more peculiar the picture becomes, so the effect can be heightened further if you attach an extra wide-angle adapter onto the lens. The ultimate is achieved if you use a 'fish-eye' adapter: these more than double the angle of view and introduce pronounced 'barrel distortion' which adds an even greater feeling of unreality to the scene. If you are considering buying one of these adapters, check first that it will work with your zoom lens without clipping the corners of the picture at full wide angle.

At the telephoto end of the zoom, the depth of the picture appears to be compressed, and this is often used by cameraman to create a claustrophobic effect. The television cliché of seemingly horrific nose-to-tail traffic congestion is one example of the deliberate use of telephoto to reduce the apparent depth of a scene – the shot of a runner trying hard to reach the camera, but making little forward progress, is another.

Trick Lenses and Filters

You can increase your range of special effects by investing in a few trick lenses and filters. These are available either singly or in boxed sets and are not expensive. Split-focus lenses, for instance, work rather like bi-focal spectacles, one half of the lens being arranged to focus on the subject in the foreground while the other half does the same for the background. Although this is not an effect, as such, it does enable you to shoot scenes where the action is taking place over an unusually large range of distances from the camera, and great depth of field is needed to keep it all sharp.

If you have a multiple-image lens, you can obtain some quite stunning visual effects. In one version of the lens, the central subject is surrounded by repeat images which can be made to gyrate round it. This is done simply by rotating the multi-lens by means of an outer ring which enables the assembly to be revolved without disturbing the setting of the camcorder lens to which it is attached. If you combine this gyratory movement with zoom in and out, you can create effects which are quite dream-like.

Trick filters come in various forms. Polaroid filters are used to eliminate unwanted reflections off water, glass and painted metals, thus allowing the camera to see through the glare to the object beneath. The amount of polarisation can be varied by rotating the filter assembly, and it can also be used to cut through atmospheric haze and to enrich the blueness of the sky.

Starburst filters are designed to put a touch of extra sparkle onto brightly reflective objects such as the shimmer on sunlit water. Also known as cross-screen filters, they consist of thin sheets of optical glass which are etched with a grid of fine cross-lines. The grid is invisible on normally-lit scenes, but produces the

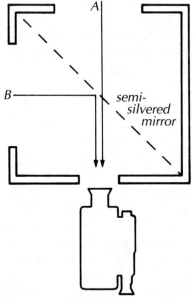

The diagram shows a semi-silvered mirror mounted at 45 degrees across the corners of a box in which apertures are provided through which the camera receives the combined images of objects at A and B. The illusion is due to the fact that the mirror acts as both a transmitter and reflector of light. Graphics or projected scenes can also be superimposed using this method.

characteristic star effect on bright points of light and can enhance the appearance of jewellery and other such items. Diffraction filters are used in a similar way, but they instead break the pinpoints of light down into the component colours of the spectrum. The effect is simple to produce, but the impact on the screen can be quite dazzling.

Filters can be employed not only to correct the colours in a scene but also to change them for effect. Orange-tinted ones will warm up the scene, and blue ones will cool it down. If the 'wrong' colour is used, for instance a red filter for a shot of countryside under a blue sky, the resulting colour shifts will make it look like the landscape of another planet, although your white balance control will do its best to correct them. Even more unusual effects can be obtained by attaching a multi-coloured filter which can be set with the colour divisions running horizontally, vertically or at an angle, and the bizarre appearance can be reinforced by switching the camcorder to a 'wrong' white balance setting.

Graduated neutral-density and colour filters change to character of a scene in more subtle ways. Rain clouds hovering overhead can be made to look even more heavily threatening and subjects can be highlighted by surrounding them with filtered backgrounds. The effect is lost if the camera is panned, however, because the filtered area shifts and the nature of the deception becomes all too apparent.

Some video cameras and camcorders are fitted with a negative/positive switch. This enables images to be viewed as though they were photographic colour-negatives, giving the scene an intensely other-worldly look – use it for dream sequences.

Special Lighting

Lighting can be rigged in various ways to produce unusual effects. We are conditioned to expect light always to shine downwards from above, and whenever this natural arrangement is reversed by lighting subjects from below, it conflicts with our instinctive feelings as to what is normal. Faces lit from below, especially if they are heavily shadowed, can appear quite alarmingly ghostly.

Shadows themselves can be powerful creators of heightened tension, as the early film makers well understood. They are an economical way of setting a scene, too. A prison atmosphere can be evoked simply by the image of bars on a wall, and the stealthy elongation of shadows can do more to suggest creeping menace than any number of clearly seen horrors.

Coloured lighting can be a potent mood inducer as any visitor to a disco will know, and the cross-lighting of scenes in opposing colours is yet another inexpensive way of changing the appearance of things. Filter gels can be obtained in almost any colour from theatrical stockists and some lighting specialists. These can be fitted over floodlights by means of special filter attachments.

Superimpositions

Because of its inherent technical complexities, the electronic superimposition of video pictures is an effect which can only be achieved through the use of rather expensive vision mixing equipment. However, semi-silvered mirrors can be utilised to carry out simple types of superimposition in camera at little cost. These mirrors, available from optical supplies specialists, are both partial reflectors and partial transmitters of light, a property which makes possible the combination of two images by optical means.

The mirror is fitted at an angle of 45° across the corners of a box, in three sides of which are cut viewing apertures. The camera is set to view object 'A' through two opposing apertures by direct transmission through the mirror. Object 'B' is placed so that its reflected image can also be seen by the camera, the 'A' and 'B' images now being superimposed on each other. The objects should be brightly lit and at roughly equal light-path distances from the camera to simplify focusing. If the lighting of the objects is dimmer-controlled, mixes and dissolves in and out can be done. 'A' and 'B' need not be solid objects, as images can be back projected through the apertures instead. With a little ingenuity, therefore, you can superimpose slide transparencies or cine film shots over each other, and if you position television screens at the apertures you can experiment with the superimposition of video pictures as well! Titles can be faded up over slide backgrounds, maps can be animated, and ghost objects can be made to appear and disappear.

The reshooting of video directly off a television screen opens up still further trick possibilities. You can not only alter the colours but also, by zooming into extreme close-ups you can reveal the line matrix of the picture which begins to disintegrate into its three-colour components and take on a thoroughly surreal appearance.

Stop Motion

If your camcorder is one of the newer ones with stop-motion recording, there are all kinds of tricks you can play. Though full frame-by-frame animation is not yet possible on amateur video equipment, the latest models come close to this ideal by making it possible to record video in bursts of very short duration (one second or less) so that pixillation effects can be achieved. Pixillation, where inanimate objects or people are made to appear and disappear or move around in a comically jerky fashion, is an old favourite in the cinema but has only just become possible on video. The best effects are probably the ones which are shot with the camera on a tripod and operated with a remote release for maximum steadiness, because the subjects then carry out their trick movements against an absolutely steady background. If, on the other hand, the pixillation is shot from off a hand-held camera, the background will pixillate too, so the choice is up to you.

Recently, digital frame-store circuitry has been developed which enables television and video pictures to be stored in solid state memory chips. These can then be reproduced in a variety of ways. Picture-in-picture displays are one example of this new technology, where moving or still images can be reproduced to a smaller size within the main picture and shifted about to different corners of the screen. Freeze-frame strobing introduces another interesting effect by which the video picture can be frozen as a single still while the sound continues as normal, or a series of stills can be flashed onto the screen at variable intervals while the sound continues unchanged. Digital zoom enlargements of the image and split-screen mirror images are but two of the increasing number of bizarre effects which are available to build into your avant-garde productions.

Production Mixers

Although these and other effects can be produced on a number of leading makes of VCR, for more comprehensive image-manipulation facilities you need to go one stage further and provide yourself with a full-scale production mixer. These units are certainly not cheap, but they allow advanced amateurs or low-budget professionals the kind of video picture editing capability which has hitherto been open only to broadcast and other major video production organisations.

One of the technical tricks which these mixers perform is the synchronisation of two incoming video signals which can then be mixed together for dissolves or wipes. The latter can be plain horizontal or vertical wipes from one video picture to the next, or they can be box or circular wipes which expand to fill the screen with the new picture. If you wish, you can make your shots look like poster-paintings or mosaics, and quite bizarre colour effects can be keyed in to completely change the appearance of the scene. Titles can also be character-generated on some mixers and superimposed on video at editing.

Desk-top Video

Some home computers can now be interfaced with video recorders, and software packages are becoming available which not only enable titles to be produced electronically, but also an increasingly imaginative range of images and abstract designs can be generated and edited onto your video tapes. These fascinating pictures can be twisted, wrapped, tilted, rotated, scrolled, bent and generally thrown about the screen, and there seems to be no limit as to what can be achieved through desk-top techniques, as this branch of the art of creative video is called.

Although character-generated titles are a useful facility to have at one's disposal, there are those who still prefer the appearance of titles which have been produced by traditional methods, that is by artwork lettering on cards. These are then photographed by camcorder either for editing in the usual way or for superimposition via a production mixer or video processor.

If you lack artistic ability, the problem of how to produce good-looking lettering can be easily solved by the use of transfer lettering which is available at stationers in a wide variety of styles and sizes.

If you intend to provide a photographic background for the title the size of this will have an influence on the title card, but one which is between 12–24 cm (5–10in) in width will be found to be the most convenient. The lettering should be contained within an area which is not greater than 90 per cent of the width and height of the card; this, and the length of the title, will determine the size of lettering to be used. You will probably find that letters with a body height of not less than 6mm (¼in) are handiest to work with. Single-word titles can be assembled from much bigger characters than this, though, if the style of the title warrants it.

The general appearance of a title should reflect the subject: an informal style would suit a domestic theme, while a documentary might call for one with a crisper look. The wording should be laid out carefully, as any deviations in the lining up of the letters will be magnified on screen. Pay great attention to the spacing – curved letters should sit closer together than those with straight edges. Aim for a balanced look: one-line titles often look best if they are set low, at about a third of the height of the screen, and titles which run to several lines should align to the left.

If you are using a pictorial background, make sure that the lettering stands out clearly against it, and that the whole design, letters and background, is harmonious and uncluttered. The colour of the lettering will depend to some extent on the colour of the background, but white is generally the easiest to read and give sthe neatest appearance. If your title background is to be a plain colour, choose pastel rather than bright primary colours to avoid possible problems with video picture-noise; a hint of texture in the colour background will also help with this.

Titles

For really individual titles that will add an extra touch of class to your movies, hand-lettered wording with artist-drawn backgrounds are well worth the effort to make. All artwork for video recordings should be kept fairly simple, though, and you may need to experiment in order to find out which techniques come over best on the screen. Anything from plain line drawings to full-colour illustrations can be tried, but cartoon style graphics in clear black line often work best with titles.

Of all title backgrounds, those with a matt finish will give least trouble with reflections when they are being photographed. The cards should be attached to a flat piece of board which can be supported vertically in a fixed position on some kind of easel or hung on the wall. At a pinch, the lighting can be window-daylight if this gives a sufficiently even spread of illuminations. A better alternative is to use a pair of ordinary household lamps in reflectors which can either be bought or made up from cardboard covered with aluminium baking foil.

Place the lamps on either side of the camcorder, which should also be firmly supported, preferably on a tripod. If you intend to do a lot of titling, a purpose-built titling arrangement may be worth obtaining; these provide adjustable mountings for both title card and camcorder, and include a pair of built-in lamp units. They are much more convenient to use than temporary set-ups.

Precise alignment and centring of the title is very important: the smallest deviation from the horizontal will be very noticeable, and this should be checked on the monitor screen, together with the focus and colour balance before you make the recording.

In this simple set-up, the title card can be pinned to a wall and lit by ordinary household lamps – anglepoise types are ideal. The camcorder is supported on a tripod and carefully lined up and centred on the title. Alternatively, a purpose-built titling unit can be made up or purchased.

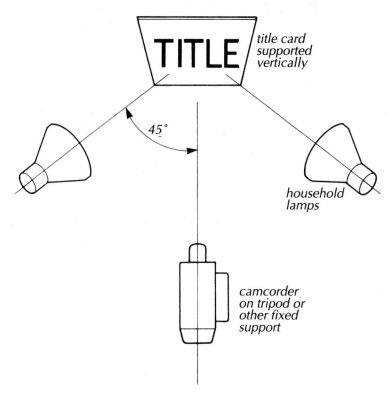

title card
supported
vertically

45°

household
lamps

camcorder
on tripod or
other fixed
support

15 Television and video overseas

Although we often watch television programmes which have been produced in countries other than our own, technically speaking television is much less of a universal medium than you might think. Worldwide, in fact, there are currently three different colour television broadcasting systems, each of which transmits its programmes to technical standards which are incompatible with the other two.

High Definition Television, when it becomes an established system, will introduce new possibilities of system incompatibility. This inevitably places limits on the interchange of television and video equipment from one country to another, and it also restricts the free exchange of pre-recorded video tapes to a considerable extent. The three established systems are PAL, NTSC and SECAM.

Colour Broadcasting Systems

PAL (Phase Alternate Line) is the system which is used in the United Kingdom. It is also widely used in Europe and in many other countries. NTSC (National Television Standards Committee) is the pioneer colour television system which was first developed in the United States of America, and it is now also used in South America, Japan and elsewhere. SECAM (Sequential Colour with Memory) is a system which was developed in France; it is still in use there, as well as in Russia and other East European countries. For a detailed list of colour television broadcast standards around the world see pages 186-187.

What does this mean for you and your camcorder when you travel abroad? How does it affect the exchange of video tapes with friends and relations overseas? Suppose that you are planning to visit the USA from the UK. On the visit, you would not be able to play back tapes off your PAL camcorder by plugging it into an American NTSC television set because the two sets of standards are totally incompatible. If you wish to be able to check your recordings in colour during the trip, you would have to take either a camcorder with a colour viewfinder, or a separate PAL-compatible portable colour monitor with you – one of the new mini-LCD-type models – so that you could be completely independent of the NTSC system. (You would still need to be able to top your rechargeable batteries from the mains, though).

The same restriction applies to PAL video recordings: the tapes will not play back on NTSC system video recorders unless the latter are multi-standard machines, which are now becoming available to domestic users. Otherwise, if you wish to send a tape from the UK to the USA, you will need to get it copied to the NTSC standard. These conversions can be carried out as a service by various facility houses which advertise in the video press. NTSC tapes can also be copied to the PAL standard.

Compataility

Although the PAL system is widely used throughout the world, the standard which is used in the UK is not quite the same as the PAL which is used in most other countries. This means that a UK camcorder will not play back correctly on a television set designed for use in these PAL countries. Happily, the differences between the various types of PAL system do not affect the playing back of video tapes. A tape recorded to any of the PAL standards will play back on any PAL machine.

The compatibility position respecting SECAM is that it is not possible to use SECAM camcorders to play back onto NTSC receivers, or vice versa. SECAM and NTSC tapes are not exchangeable either; however, PAL tapes will play back on SECAM machines, and the same is true for SECAM tapes on PAL machines.

In short, if you wish to send your video recordings abroad, you can do this if the recipients have a video machine of the same

NATIONAL COLOUR
TELEVISION STANDARDS

Country	Standard	Country	Standard
Abu Dhabi	PAL	France	SECAM
Alaska	NTSC	Germany (East)	SECAM
Algeria	PAL	Germany (West)	PAL
Argentina	PAL	Ghana	PAL
Australia	PAL	Gibraltar	PAL
Austria	PAL	Greece	PAL
Bahamas	NTSC	Greenland	NTSC
Bahrain	PAL	Haiti	NTSC
Bangladesh	PAL	Hawaii	NTSC
Barbados	NTSC	Honduras	NTSC
Belgium	PAL	Hong Kong	PAL I
Bermuda	NTSC	Hungary	SECAM
Brazil	PAL M	Iceland	PAL
Bulgaria	SECAM	India	PAL
Burma	NTSC	Indonesia	PAL
Canada	NTSC	Iran	SECAM
Canary Islands	PAL	Iraq	SECAM
Chile	NTSC	Ireland (Eire)	PAL I
Channel Islands	PAL I	Israel	PAL
China	PAL	Italy	PAL
Colombia	NTSC	Jamaica	NTSC
Cuba	NTSC	Japan	NTSC
Cyprus	PAL	Kenya	PAL
Czechoslovakia	SECAM	Korea (South)	NTSC
Denmark	PAL	Kuwait	PAL
Dubai	PAL	Laos	SECAM
Ecuador	NTSC	Lebanon	SECAM
Egypt	SECAM	Liberia	PAL
Finland	PAL	Liechtenstein	PAL

Country	Standard	Country	Standard
Madagascar	SECAM	Sudan	PAL
Madeira	PAL	Sweden	PAL
Malaysia	PAL	Switzerland	PAL
Malta	PAL	Taiwan	NTSC
Mexico	NTSC	Tanzania	PAL I
Monaco	SECAM	Thailand	PAL
Mongolia	SECAM	Tibet	PAL
Morocco	SECAM	Tunisia	SECAM
Mozambique	PAL I	Turkey	PAL
Netherlands	PAL	Uganda	PAL
New Zealand	PAL	UAE	PAL
Nicaragua	NTSC	UK	PAL I
Nigeria	PAL	Uruguay	PAL
Norway	PAL	USA	NTSC
Pakistan	PAL	Venezuela	NTSC
Panama	NTSC	Yemen	PAL
Paraguay	PAL	Yugoslavia	PAL
Peru	NTSC	Zaire	SECAM
Philippines	NTSC	Zambia	PAL
Poland	SECAM	Zimbabwe	PAL
Portugal	PAL		
Puerto Rico	NTSC		
Romania	SECAM		
Russia	SECAM		
Saudia Arabia	SECAM		
Singapore	PAL		
South Africa	PAL I		
Spain	PAL		
Sri Lanka	PAL		

format and able to operate with the television system on which it was recorded.

If, while you are abroad, you are tempted to buy 'bargain' video equipment, make sure first that it is suitable for use on your home electrical power supply, and is designed to use on your national television standard. Otherwise, when you return you may find that your purchase is unusable without expensive conversion, if at all.

Care of equipment and tapes

The day-to-day care of camcorders and other video equipment is largely a matter of common sense. Some of the camcorder 'do nots' have already been mentioned in earlier chapters: do not allow moisture or dust to enter the body-shell, do not subject it to extremes of heat, cold or humidity, do not subject it to mechanical shocks. Given that these elementary precautions are followed, you should have little trouble with your camcorder. In spite of its complex mechanisms and circuitry, it is in fact a robust and reliable piece of equipment which will survive the hazards of normal usage.

Transporting Equipment

Your video gear is probably more at risk while it is being transported from place to place than when it is switched on and running. A camcorder is best carried around in a well-padded bag made specially for the purpose; in the car, it should be held on a passenger's knees or securely wedged into place on a seat, not

Caution

Take care of your camcorder:

! *Do not allow moisture/dust to enter body-shell.*
! *Do not subject it to extremes of heat/cold/humidity.*
! *Do not subject it to mechanical shocks.*

dumped on the floor or in the boot where it may be subjected to severe vibration or jolting.

Care of Lenses and Batteries

Camcorder lenses should be kept covered at all times except when actually in use. Fit a UV or plain glass filter over the lens to protect it from contact with grease, grime and the elements. If in spite of your best care the lens on your camcorder does need cleaning, this is a job which you can do for yourself provided that you set about it in the right way. If the problem is simply dust on the lens, this can be cleaned off with a special blower-brush which should be lightly applied and worked outwards from the centre of the lens to the edges. For greasy smears, finger-marks or sticky seaspray deposits, use one of the proprietary lens cleaning fluids applied with a lint-free optical cloth or lens tissues. Employ light pressure and work from the centre outwards.

Rechargeable camcorder batteries are expensive to replace, but their lives can be extended if they are treated with care. Pay particular attention to the instructions concerning the recharging routine; most batteries now require to be discharged via a battery discharger before recharging to prolong their working lives and to retain their full current capacities. Some battery chargers include a 'refresh' feature.

Storage of Tapes

The storage of video tapes is another area where a little thought and care will pay dividends in terms of both tape life and reduced wear and tear on video heads. Fortunately, the ideal conditions are similar to those which you like for yourself – an even air temperature of 15–20°C (60–70°F), dust-free and with low relative humidity. Hence, the conditions in the average living room are just about right. Store the cassettes either in their cardboard boxes or in library cases, and keep them upright rather than flat. This is to reduce the risk of damage to the edges of tapes if they are allowed to come into prolonged contact with the reel sides.

Try to avoid dropping a tape cassette, not only because of the risk of physical damage but also because the magnetic recording itself may be adversely affected if the tape is subject to mechanical shocks. Magnetic print-through from one coil of tape to the next is not really a problem with good quality tapes, but it does no harm to rewind them once a year just to be on the safe side. Keep your tapes away from strong magnetic fields, and remove the safety-tabs from cassettes containing important recordings to prevent the risk of accidental erasure.

Do not touch the surface of a video tape with your hand: grease will be transferred to it and thence to the video heads where it will affect the quality of the recording and may even cause damage. Use only high quality tapes of known brands for your recordings: poor quality tapes may increase head wear and will probably shed oxide particles.

Cleaning Heads

Even the best tapes shed some oxide, however, and although the rotating video heads in camcorders and VCRs are to a large extent self-cleaning they may need attention from time to time. There is much to be said for an annual service which should include not only cleaning of the heads and tape guides but also any adjustments and re-alignments which may be necessary. Failing this regular servicing, dirt deposits on the heads and tape guides may result in 'snow' on the picture and partial loss of sound; tape mistracking problems may also be experienced. Some machines now incorporate an automatic head cleaning facility.

If you prefer, you can clean the tape path on your camcorder or VCR for yourself by the use of one of the proprietary cleaning cassettes which are on the market. Some of these use a dry cleaning agent, while others use a wet system; both types are effective, but over-use may lead to premature head wear and the instructions should be followed meticulously.

Glossary

Accessory shoe clip for the attachment of lighting or other items to camcorders.

AGC automatic gain control – maintains video picture exposure and sound at standard levels.

Ambient noise the noise background at a location.

Amplitude the level of a signal.

Analogue signal in wave form as distinct from digital.

Aperture the amount of opening of a lens iris.

ASO Active Sideband Optimum, a picture enhancement system.

Assemble edit the sequential recording or re-recording of video in correct shot order.

ATF Auto Tracking Focus, a system which moves the focus zone to follow the subject round the frame.

Attenuator resistance for reducing the strength of an electronic signal.

Audio dub erasure of the original synchronised sound by the substitution of new sound.

AV audio-visual; sockets for video and audio in/out.

Backlight under-exposure of the main subject due to light coming from behind it.

Backspace technique whereby camcorders and VCRs make 'clean' edits.

BCU big close-up.

BLC backlight compensation.

Boom extension arm for mounting microphones etc; the echoey quality of room acoustics.

Bounce light the illumination of a scene by reflected light.

BNC bayonet type of connector commonly used for video signal leads.

Cardioid microphone a microphone with forward directional characteristics.

Camcorder one-piece combined video camera and recorder.

CCD solid state image sensor for camcorders and video cameras.

Chrominance the colour component of a video signal.

Colour bars video colour test signal of eight vertical bars: white, yellow, cyan, green, magenta, red, blue, black.

Colour temperature the colour quality of a light source.

Compatibility the degree to which video recordings can be played back on other equipment as affected by format etc.

Component video the video signal transmitted and recorded as separate luminance and chrominance components.

Composite video combined luminance and chrominance video signal as outputted by camcorders except the super-format types.

Continuity the logical progression of actions or consistency of appearance from shot to shot.

Contrast the range of brightness from highlight to shadow in a picture.

Control track pulse-track to synchronise the head-drum to the picture signals on a video tape.

CU close-up.

Cue/review forward or reverse picture-search replay of a video tape.

Cutaway the editing-in of material additional to the main shot to permit a scene to be shortened or to hide a jump-cut.

Cut-in similar to a cutaway, but the edited-in material is a close-up detail to something within the main shot.

Cut on action a cut which carries a continuous action over from one shot to the next.

dB unit of sound volume, signal strength and signal-to-noise ratio.

Depth of field the range of distances within a shot which are in sharp focus.

Diffuser filter for softening the effects of direct lighting.

Digital effects video effects such as wipes, strobing, etc., produced by digital signal processing.

Digital signal pulse-type signal as distinct from one which is in 'wave' form.

Dolby noise reduction system for audio recording.

Dropout picture fault caused by dirt on the tape.

Dubbing the copying of a recording onto another tape.

Dynamic microphone a type of microphone which works on the moving-coil principle.

Edit controller a unit connected between (eg) a camcorder and a VCR which controls both machines in an editing set-up.

Edit in camera the technique of shooting video in sequence order and to length.

Effects background sound for dubbing onto a recording.

Electret microphone a type of microphone which works on the charged capacitor principle.

Establishing shot a wide shot (long shot) which is used to open a sequence.

Eyeline the direction in which the subject is looking.

Fade in/out increase/decrease in the brightness of the video picture from/to black or white.

Fill light soft light to fill shadows produced by the main or key light.

Filter transparent material used to change the colour or intensity of light.

Flying erase video erase heads which are mounted on the head-drum of a camcorder to give picture edits free of disturbance.

FM audio hi-fi sound recording system.

Format video tape cassette system, eg VHS.

Frame a complete scan of video picture.

Frame advance frame-by-frame playback of video pictures.

Generation each successive dub or copy of an original recording.

Genlock device used to synchronise video or computer input signals for editing.

Glitch picture disturbance at edits.

Graphic equaliser device for selective filtering of particular frequencies from a sound signal.

Halogen quartz/IQ high-efficiency type of lamp used in video lights.

Helical scan the laying of diagonal signal tracks along the length of a video tape.

Hi8 high band version of the 8mm format.

Highlight the brightest part of a picture.

High-speed shutter facility on a camcorder for shooting blur-free pictures of rapidly moving objects.

Horizontal resolution a measure of video picture quality.

Insert edit the over-recording of new video material onto a video tape.

Jack type of plug used for audio connections.

Jitter unstable video picture.

Jog/shuttle dial control found on edit VCRs for accurate frame selection.

Jump-cut an edit which interrupts the continuity of a continuous action.

Key light the main light which provides the modelling for a subject and sets the exposure level.

LANC/Control L a type of edit remote control connection used on 8mm machines.

LCD liquid crystal display; used for tape counters etc.

LCD screen miniature colour screen as used on colour viewfinders.

Line in/out the signal level at which video and audio is transferred for dubbing.

Low band term describing the recording and playback quality of Standard VHS and 8mm machines as compared with high band.

LP long-play, half-speed recording which doubles the runtime of a cassette.

LS long shot.

Luminance the monochrome (brightness) component of a video signal.

Lux the intensity of illumination of a surface.

Macro ultra close-up setting of a zoom lens.

Master first generation video recording (ie camera original).

Mic microphone.

Mix dissolving transition from one picture or sound to another.

Modulator (RF) combines video and audio signals into a form which can be fed to a television set via its aerial socket.

Monitor television set which can accept separate video and audio signals.

MS medium shot.

Noise unwanted additions to pictures and sound due to inferior signal quality or clogged heads.

NTSC the colour television system used in the USA and elsewhere (see pages 186-187).

Omnidirectional microphone microphone equally sensitive to sound coming from all directions.

PAL the colour television system used in the UK and elsewhere (see pages 186-187).

Pan horizontal rotation of the camera.

Pan head swivelling device mounted on a tripod to enable the camera to be panned and tilted.

PCM Pulse Code Modulation, a hi-fi audio system used on some 8mm machines.

Photoflood type of tungsten lamp used for photographic work.

PIP Picture in Picture effect produced by digital signal processing technology.

Pixel individual element forming the picture on a TV or LCD screen.

Post-production edit the editing of video material after the shoot has been completed.

Power zoom operation of the zoom on a lens by servo control.

Programme autoexposure system of shutter and aperture control to optimise camcorder recording quality under different conditions such as sports action and portraiture.

Quasi-S-VHS playback a system whereby some VHS VCRs can play back S-VHS recordings at low-band quality.

RCTC Rewritable Consumer Time Code system used for video editing.

Real time counter VCR tape counter reading in hours, minutes and seconds of tape time.

RF radio frequency – see Modulator.

RGB Red, Green, Blue components of video signal.

Scart multi-pin connector for video and audio input and output signals.

SECAM the colour television system used in France and elsewhere (see pages 186-187).

Sequence the succession of shots in an orderly arrangement.

Shooting script a movie script which gives precise details of the camera angles, action etc.

Shutter speed the normal (electronic) shutter speed of a PAL camcorder is 1/50th sec; high shutter speeds are now available on many machines.

Still frame the display of a single frame of picture.

Story board the sequences of a movie set out in a series of rough drawings.

S-VHS the high band version of VHS.

S-video terminal a connector used to feed high band signals between a camcorder or VCR to a monitor screen.

Sync synchronisation

Synchro edit facility which enables source and record video machines to be started in synchronisation for editing.

Synopsis the outline, or 'treatment', for a movie.

Telecine device for transferring cine film onto video.

Telephoto lens long focal length lens for magnifying distant subjects.

Tie-clip microphone miniature electret microphone.

Tilt rotation of the camera vertically.

Time code an electronic 'labelling' of each frame for high accuracy video editing.

Treatment see Synopsis.

Trick play playback of video at anything other than normal forward speed.

Tungsten name given to interior lighting other than fluorescent.

Unidirectional microphone sensitive mainly to sounds coming from the forward direction.

VCR video cassette recorder.

VHS popular video format using 12.7mm ('/₂in) tape.

VHS-C compact VHS format.

Video 8 video format using 8-mm tape.

VITC Vertical Interval Time Code system used for video editing.

VU meter used for measurement of audio signal levels.

Watt unit of electrical power.

White balance system for adjusting the colour balance on a camcorder.

Wide angle lens short focal length lens for reducing the distance at which a scene can be photographed.

Wildtrack unsynchronised source of sound effects for dubbing.

Zoom lens of variable focal length.

Index